Muffles' Measurement Models

Part One: Customary U.S. Units

Catherine Twomey Fosnot
Catherine Henchey

New Perspectives on Learning, LLC
1194 Ocean Avenue
New London, CT 06320

Table of Contents

Unit Overview

This unit is the first of two related, companion units for grade 4 focused on the development of measurement. This unit focuses on the Customary U.S. units; the second focuses on place value and the metric system. Muffles, a baker, is introduced to students in *Muffles' Truffles*, a previous CFLM unit that provides various opportunities to explore multiplication using arrays.

Muffles returns in *Muffles' Measurement Models (Parts One and Two).* He expands his business and several problems related to measurement arise. For one, he needs conversion tables for his recipes! Children explore measurement conversions and develop several tables for converting liters to milliliters, pounds to ounces, inches to feet and yards, centimeters to meters and kilometers, grams to kilograms, minutes to hours and seconds, and dollars to dimes and pennies. Children are asked to select and use an appropriate measurement unit, to compare and relate the measurements, to construct the need for decomposition of units into smaller units, and to use operations to convert units. The models used throughout are the double number line for equivalence and the ratio table for scaling and proportional reasoning. The units are designed to align with the CCSS Standards of Mathematical Practice and the following core objectives:

Measurement & Data 4.MD: Solve problems involving measurement and conversion of measurements.

CCSS.Math.Content.4.MD.A.1

Know relative sizes of measurement units within one system of units including km, m, cm; kg, g; lb, oz.; l, ml; hr, min, sec. Within a single system of measurement, express measurements in a larger unit in terms of a smaller unit. Record measurement equivalents in a two-column table. *For example, know that 1 ft is 12 times as long as 1 in. Express the length of a 4 ft snake as 48 in. Generate a conversion table for feet and inches listing the number pairs (1, 12), (2, 24), (3, 36), …*

CCSS.Math.Content.4.MD.A.2

Use the four operations to solve word problems involving distances, intervals of time, liquid volumes, masses of objects, and money, including problems involving simple fractions or decimals, and problems that require expressing measurements given in a larger unit in terms of a smaller unit. Represent measurement quantities using diagrams such as number line diagrams that feature a measurement scale.

The Landscape of Learning

BIG IDEAS
❖ Smaller units produce a greater value than larger units
❖ Larger units can encompass (and be decomposed into) smaller units
❖ Unitizing
❖ Equivalent measurements can be exchanged
❖ Place value patterns occur when multiplying or dividing by the base
❖ Proportional reasoning

STRATEGIES
❖ Uses standard units and counts
❖ Chooses appropriate unit in relation to object being measured
❖ Decomposes and switches units when needed
❖ Converts using skip counting
❖ Converts using partial products
❖ Scales by doubling
❖ Scales by halving
❖ Scales using place value patterns
❖ Generalized scaling using the operations of multiplication and division

MODELS
❖ Double Number Line
❖ Ratio Table

The Mathematical Landscape

By fourth grade most children have become fairly competent in measuring. For example, when measuring length they iterate a single unit (such as a ruler or meter stick). They place the units back-to-back without gaps and they know the size of the unit matters—smaller units produce a greater value than larger units, yet the measurements are equivalent. They may even know that time is measured in minutes and hours and weight is measured in grams, kilograms, and/or pounds and ounces. However, they usually have little understanding of the exact relationships of the units, for example the exact relationship of inches to feet and feet to yards, or centimeters to the meter stick, or liters to milliliters, etc. They also do not yet have efficient strategies for converting from one unit to another.

The investigations in these two companion units involve children in choosing appropriate tools for more exact measurement and converting from one unit to another. *Muffles' Measurement Models, Part One* focuses on the Customary U.S. measurement tools and conversion within that system. *Muffles' Measurement Models, Part Two* focuses on place value and the metric system. Both units provide children with partially filled out measurement tables. To become able to convert easily from one measure to another, students need a complex network of relations comprised of some big ideas, strategies, and models as shown on the Landscape of Learning on page 10. A description of each follows.

As children explore the investigations within the two units, several big ideas arise. These include:

❖ *Smaller units produce a greater value than larger units*
❖ *Larger units can encompass (and be decomposed into) smaller units*
❖ *Unitizing*
❖ *Equivalent measurements can be exchanged*
❖ *Place value patterns occur when multiplying or dividing by the base*
❖ *Proportional reasoning*

❖ *Smaller units produce a greater value than larger units*

Within a single measurable attribute (mass, volume, time, length, etc.) there are both large and small standardized units. As children measure with these standard units, they construct the idea that when larger units are used the overall measurement will be a smaller number and reciprocally, when smaller units are used the overall measurement will be a greater number.

❖ *Larger units can encompass (and be decomposed into) smaller units*

Iterated smaller units (like inches) can be grouped into larger units (like feet), which in turn can be grouped into yards. As children come to realize that if larger units are used, less would be needed, they can more appropriately choose a unit to use to measure a given object. A 10 ft line might better be measured with a foot-long ruler than with inches, whereas a line less than a foot long might be best to measure in inches. On the other hand, a larger unit may need to be decomposed for exactness. For example, measuring a 10 ft line with a yardstick would require decomposing the last yard into feet.

❖ *Unitizing*

With number, unitizing a group of 10 objects into 1 ten is a big idea. It requires multiplicative thinking as children grapple to understand 132, not just as 100 + 30 + 2, but as 13 tens, plus 2, and later as 13.2 tens. The case is no different with measurement units. As children compose and decompose units, they come to understand that a kilometer can simultaneously be seen as 1,000 meters, or as 100,000 centimeters. A yard can be seen as 3 feet, or as 36 inches.

❖ Equivalent measurements can be exchanged

Once children construct conservation of length and unitizing and have had ample opportunities to work with a variety of measurement units, they begin to understand that various units can be used to describe length and distance (or mass, volume, and time), and that equivalent pieces can be exchanged. For example, time can be measured in hours or in minutes: 1½ hours = 90 minutes. One pint plus one cup is equivalent to 1½ pints. Both measurements are correct and may be interchanged to compare or more exactly describe the amount.

❖ *Place value patterns occur when multiplying or dividing by the base*

Our decimal, or "base-10" number system, is built on tens—each successive place value to the left is generated by multiplying by ten (or dividing, as you move right). The metric system is similarly based on 10 and, along with money, affords ample opportunities for children to multiply and divide by the base. Precisely because multiplication is commutative, an interesting thing happens when students multiply by the base: the factor "moves over" to the appropriate column. For example, $10 \times 4 = 4 + 4 + 4 + 4 + 4 + 4 + 4 + 4 + 4 + 4 = 40$. The result of 40 seems amazing to students, who often say that they "added a zero," or refer to the pattern as the zero trick. The reason this works is that the 10 groups of 4 can also be thought of as 4 groups of 10—so the 4 is placed into the tens column to show that value and the unitizing of 40 into 4 groups of 10. It is important to support students in exploring why place value patterns occur—to help them construct how place value and the commutative property are involved. As students explore the metric system these ideas are extended further, as now they are multiplying and dividing by 100 and 1,000 as well.

❖ *Proportional reasoning*

As children work to convert one unit into another, they are developing proportional reasoning. They are dealing with ratios. The logic is: if 100 centimeters equal 1 meter, then 500 centimeters equal 5 meters. Scaling both units up proportionally keeps the conversion rate constant.

STRATEGIES

As you work with the activities in this unit, you will notice that students will use many strategies to solve the problems that are posed to them. Here are some strategies to notice:

- ❖ *Uses standard units and counts*
- ❖ *Chooses an appropriate unit in relation to object being measured*
- ❖ *Decomposes and switches units when needed*
- ❖ *Converts using skip counting*
- ❖ *Converts using partial products*
- ❖ *Scales by doubling*
- ❖ *Scales by halving*
- ❖ *Scales using place value patterns*
- ❖ *Generalized scaling using the operations of multiplication and division*

❖ Uses standard units and counts

Once children construct the idea that a standard unit is necessary for reliable measurement comparisons, they carefully mark the endpoints and count. When asked to convert to a different size unit within the same system, they do not convert, however. They just switch tools, measure again, and count.

❖ Chooses appropriate unit in relation to object being measured

Once children are comfortable understanding a variety of tools they begin to become aware that certain tools have limitations and assets. They no longer just choose a tool and estimate the leftover. They know different tools allow for exactness when needed and they choose an appropriate tool to work with depending on the task.

❖ Decomposes and switches units when needed

Once children construct the big idea that equivalent measurements can be exchanged, a multitude of possible conversions results. Something that measures 48 inches is equivalent in length to something that measures 4 feet. But also, something that measures 1 ft 6 inches can be thought of as 1.5 feet, as 18 inches, or as ½ of a yard. With the metric system, something that measures a meter plus 50 cm can be thought of as 1.5 meters, 150 cm, 15 decimeters, or as 1 ½ meters. Some children may even become intrigued with the relationship between a centimeter and an inch. The conversion rate of 2.54 centimeters = 1 inch is quite close to 2 ½ cm for every inch, and you may find some of your children saying 5 cm is the same as 2 inches, so 10 cm must be 4 inches, etc. Although this is not an exact conversion, encourage it, as it is a great estimate and an early form of proportional reasoning! A pound is equal to 0.45 kilograms, so 2 pounds equal 0.90 kilos, and 4 pounds are 1.8 kilos. Encourage this scaling even though it will not formally be a focus until grade 5.

❖ Converts using skip counting

Skip counting is an advance from counting. Rather than exchanging tools and measuring again, children skip count. For example, to convert 30 yards into feet, children skip count by threes; to convert meters into centimeters, they skip count by hundreds.

❖ Converts using partial products

Using partial products is an advance over skip counting. Knowing that the conversion of 15 yards into feet requires 15 x 3, students might use (10 x 3) + (5 x 3).

❖ Scales by doubling

Doubling is the place most children start when they begin to use proportional reasoning. It is the bridge between additive and multiplicative structuring. If 1 foot is equal to 12 inches, then 2 feet must equal 24 inches. It is a bridge to more generalized scaling because the doubling can still be seen as 12 + 12.

❖ Scales by halving

Halving is similar in terms of being a bridge, but doubling is usually easier in the same way that multiplication is easier for children than division.

❖ Scales using place value patterns

Once students construct the big idea that place value patterns occur when multiplying or dividing by the base, they recognize that the metric system presents many opportunities to take advantage of the place value structure. As students develop their proportional reasoning within the metric system, they will soon begin multiplying and dividing by 10, 100, and 1,000 to scale and convert between units.

❖ Generalized scaling using the operations of multiplication and division

Scaling is an advance over partial products, doubling, and halving as now multiplicative structuring is truly at play. Once the critical precursors (place value patterns, unitizing, proportional reasoning and multiplicative structuring) have been constructed, generalized scaling becomes automatic. In the metric system, if 1 kilogram is 1000 grams, then 4 kilograms equals 4000 grams and 8 kilograms equals 8000 grams using place value. In the Customary U.S. system the patterns are not as automatic, but each unit is still scaled up proportionally using multiplication, or scaled down as the case may require.

MATHEMATICAL MODELING

Initially models emerge as a representation *of* a situation; later they are used by teachers to represent children's computation strategies. Ultimately they are appropriated by children as powerful tools *for* thinking (Gravemeijer, 1999). Two models are used in *Muffles' Measurement Models (Parts 1 and 2)*: the double number line and the ratio table.

❖ Model of a situation

The double open number line model is introduced as a representation of the equivalence of linear units of distance. This is a powerful model for exploring grouping, unitizing, and equivalence. The model encourages a linear representation of numbers and number operations for children that is powerful for developing mental arithmetic strategies (Beishuizen 1993; Klein, Beishuizen, and Treffers 2002). The line can represent the measurement tools showing both the unit and the grouping (a foot-long ruler as 12 inches, and a yardstick as both 3 feet and 36 inches.) The meter stick shows the centimeters and decimeters (often inches as well) to support grouping, equivalence, and the algebraic strategy of substituting an equivalent expression. Using models like this supports converting from one unit to another effectively. See the figure below:

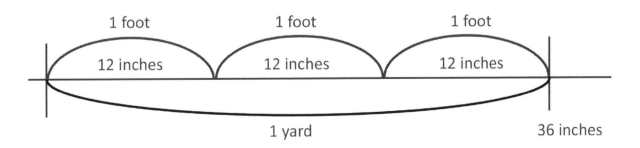

A second model used in both units is the ratio table. The ratio table emerges as Muffles' Charts—charts that help Patricio with Muffles' recipes and other needed conversions.

Pounds	Ounces
1	16
2	32
½	8
1 ½	24

The ratio table supports children to think proportionally, to use partial products, and to scale up or down keeping the rates constant.

❖ Model of Students' Strategies

Children benefit from seeing the teacher model their strategies. Once the model has been introduced as a representation of the situation, you can use it to model children's strategies as they convert. Notes are provided within the unit to help you do this.

❖ Model as a Tool for Thinking

Eventually children will be able to use the open double number line and the ratio table as tools—for thinking about measurement, and about multiplication and division in general. They will be able to imagine number as measurements on a number line and mentally mark lengths (and jumps) in various configurations. They will understand how equivalent length sections can be exchanged and the strategy of exchanging equivalent sections will become automatic. They will also have become skilled measurers: measuring competently, knowing the need for identical units and consistent relationships between units, knowing how to partition units into smaller equal parts, and knowing how to convert fluently. They will be able to employ proportional reasoning using a ratio table, which in time will become a powerful tool for representing input/output, linear functions, and even the graphing of points as Cartesian coordinates.

Lastly, note the difference between additive and multiplicative structuring. Early in development when children are using strategies based on skip counting and/or repeated addition they are modeling the problem additively. When they begin to scale and use proportional reasoning a major shift has occurred. They are now modeling the problem multiplicatively. Another example of additive structuring is finding that 3 meters = 30 decimeters by adding 10 + 10 + 10. In contrast, multiplicative structuring would be scaling and immediately using place value patterns: 3 meters = 30 decimeters = 300 centimeters, etc.

A graphic of the full landscape of learning for systems of measurement is provided on page 10. The purpose of the graphic is to allow you to see the longer journey of students' measurement development and to place your work with these two companion units within the scope of this long-term development. You may also find the graphic helpful as a way to record the progress of individual students for yourself. Each landmark can be shaded in as you find evidence in a student's work and in what the student says— evidence that a landmark strategy, big idea, or way of modeling has been constructed. Or, you may prefer to use our web-based app (www.NewPerspectivesOnAssessment.com) to document your children's growth digitally. In a very real sense, you will be recording the individual pathways your students take as they develop as young mathematicians.

References and Resources

Beishuizen, Meindert (1993). Mental strategies and materials or models for addition and subtraction up to 100 in Dutch second grades. *Journal for Research in Mathematics Education, 24,* 294–323.

Gravemeijer, Koeno (1999). How emergent models may foster the constitution of formal mathematics. *Mathematical Thinking and Learning 1* (2): 155–77.

Klein, Anton S., Meindert Beishuizen, and Adri Treffers. (2002). The empty number line in Dutch second grade, In *Lessons learned from research,* eds. Judith Sowder and Bonnie Schapelle. Reston, VA: NCTM.

SYSTEMS OF MEASUREMENT

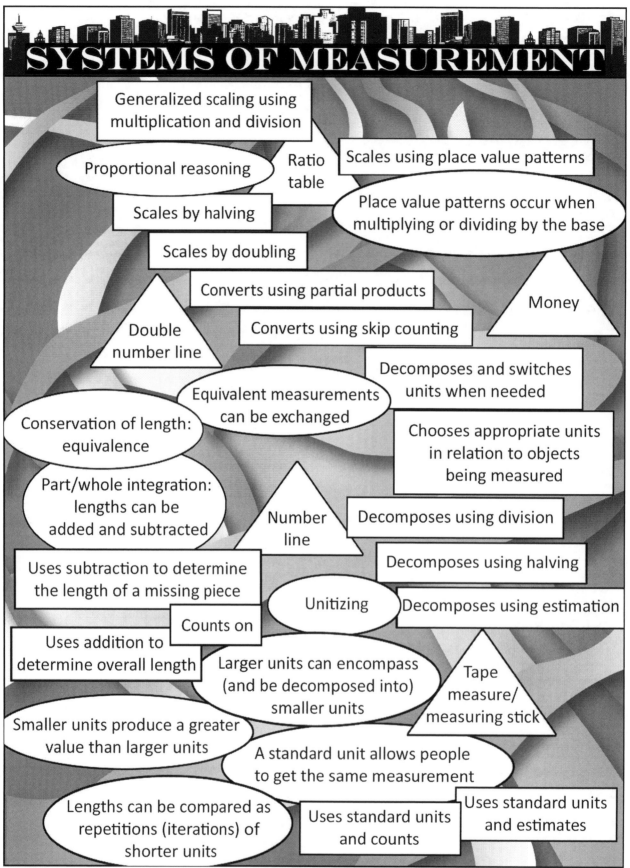

Generalized scaling using multiplication and division

Proportional reasoning

Ratio table

Scales using place value patterns

Scales by halving

Place value patterns occur when multiplying or dividing by the base

Scales by doubling

Converts using partial products

Money

Double number line

Converts using skip counting

Decomposes and switches units when needed

Equivalent measurements can be exchanged

Conservation of length: equivalence

Chooses appropriate units in relation to objects being measured

Part/whole integration: lengths can be added and subtracted

Number line

Decomposes using division

Uses subtraction to determine the length of a missing piece

Decomposes using halving

Unitizing

Decomposes using estimation

Counts on

Uses addition to determine overall length

Larger units can encompass (and be decomposed into) smaller units

Tape measure/ measuring stick

Smaller units produce a greater value than larger units

A standard unit allows people to get the same measurement

Lengths can be compared as repetitions (iterations) of shorter units

Uses standard units and counts

Uses standard units and estimates

The landscape of learning: systems of measurement on the horizon showing landmark strategies (rectangles), big ideas (ovals), and models (triangles).

MUFFLES' MEASUREMENT MODELS PART ONE: CUSTOMARY U.S. UNITS

DAY ONE

MUFFLES' CUSTOMERS

Materials Needed

Muffles' Truffles Posters (Appendices A1 and A2)

Patricio's Tape Measure (Appendix B for display and one copy per student)

Pencils

Drawing paper or several sheets of copy paper

Blank Chart Paper for posters (sticky note style is best as it makes taping on the walls unnecessary)

Markers

This unit begins with the introduction (or re-introduction) of Muffles, a chocolatier. If you and your students have previously worked through the unit *Muffles' Truffles*, the character won't be new to your students. But for others, Muffles and his truffles shop will be a new context. It is not necessary to have done the earlier unit. In that one, students designed a variety of blueprints for some new boxes of truffles and the array model for multiplication emerged.

In contrast, this unit has measurement as its goal. It begins with a description of the popularity of Muffles' truffles and the long line of customers at his door every day. A reporter from the local newspaper is doing a story on the popularity of Muffles' shop and Patricio is asked to provide measurements on the length of the line outside the door for the story: what measurement tool should he use, and just how long is the line?

Day One Outline

Developing the Context

❖ Tell the story of Muffles and his shop using Appendices A1 and A2.

❖ Facilitate a discussion on what tool might be best for Patricio to use to measure the line.

❖ Continue the story using Appendix B and send students off in pairs to figure out the length of the line in yards, feet, and inches.

Supporting the Investigation

❖ Confer with children as they work, noting the strategies they use and how they convert.

❖ Support students to note that as the units of measure increase in size, the amount of units needed decreases, and the arithmetic becomes easier. Encourage them to explain why.

❖ As students finish, ask them to prepare a poster to convince others of their solutions and important things they have noticed. These posters will be used on Day Two in a gallery walk and congress.

Developing the Context

Appendix A1 provides a picture of Muffles that you can use to introduce (or re-introduce) him to your class as you tell the following story:

> **Tech Tip**
>
> To develop the context, many teachers take a photo of Appendix A with a cell phone or iPad and project it. Others use a document camera to project the page onto a whiteboard or screen.

Muffles is a chocolatier who has a small truffles shop. He makes truffles and packages them in boxes of ten. When he first opened his shop, he had only a few customers—his family and friends. His truffles were so delicious, so delectable, that soon his customers couldn't stop eating them. They also couldn't stop talking about the most delicious truffles in the world. They told their friends, who in turn told their friends, who in turn told their friends, and before Muffles knew it he had so many customers he could hardly keep up with the demand for truffles. Long lines of people waited outside his door; sometimes the line even snaked around the corner. Sometimes there were so many customers that Muffles ran out of truffles. What sad faces! What disappointment!

[Show Appendix A2 as you continue with the story.]

Muffles' shop is soon the talk of the town and a reporter from the local newspaper decides to do a story about it. He asks Muffles how long the line is each day outside of his shop. Muffles has several measurement tools in his shop. He and his assistant, Patricio, discuss which tool would be best for the job.

[This is a nice place to stop and facilitate a discussion on which tool would be best for the job and why. As children discuss their ideas, note their familiarity with each tool and whether they know the purpose of each.]

Pass out Appendix B (one copy to each student) and use it to continue with the story. Ensure that children understand the picture of the line and how it depicts what Patricio did with the tape measure. Assign math partners and send students off to investigate what Muffles should tell the reporter. Provide drawing paper and pencils in case students wish to redraw the line and use it as a tool as they work.

Supporting the Investigation

As students begin to work, note first with a quick look around if all students are engaged and understand the context. Work first to ensure students understand the context—what Patricio did with the tape measure and why—and then sit and confer with a few pairs as they work.

If any students complain that they don't know how to start, you might remind them that mathematicians often start by trying to model the problem. Two models have been subtly introduced by the context and are consciously depicted on Appendix B—the open number line and the ratio table. Often as children model the problem they make use of these. For example, Figure 1.1 shows the use of the open number line. These students are using it as a double number line with the inches on the bottom and the feet on the top. On their paper they draw a second number line to show the feet and the yards. Each jump of 3 feet represents a yard.

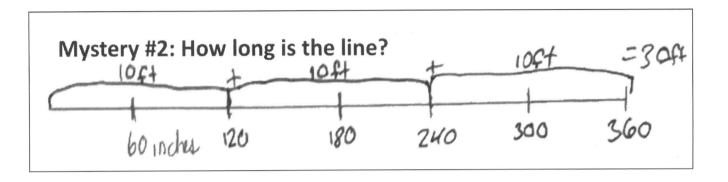

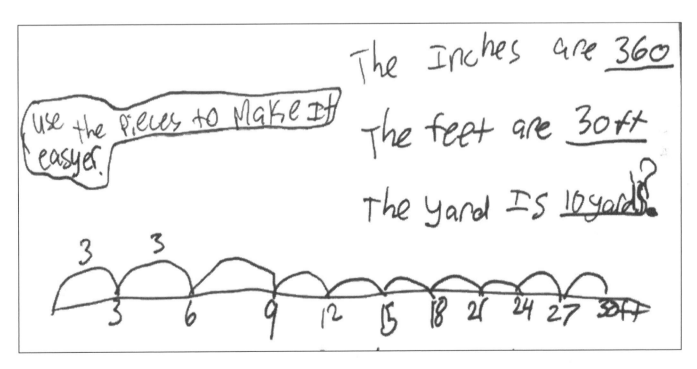

Figure 1.1: Using the Open Number Line as a Tool for Thinking

In Figure 1.2, two samples of work show examples of how students might use the ratio table.

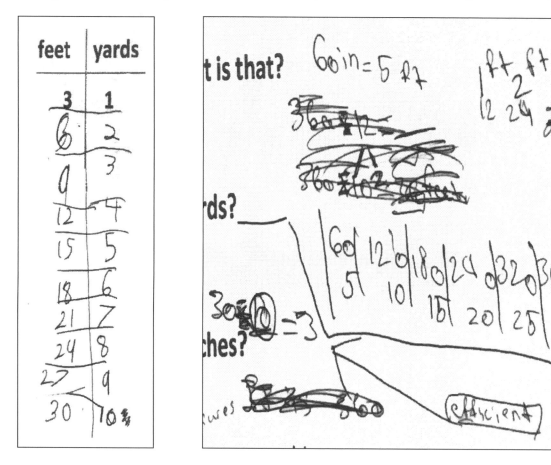

Figure 1.2: Using the Ratio Table as a Tool for Thinking

As you sit and confer with students who begin by modeling the situation, celebrate what an insight it was to make use of a model as a tool. To challenge them to work on the model more efficiently you might ask them if, when they got to the third line and noted that it was 180 inches (15 feet), they could have used this information to get to the sixth line (the endpoint). Using a doubling strategy would eliminate some steps: if the halfway point is 15 feet, then the endpoint is 30 feet; if 15 feet is 180 inches, then 30 feet is 360 inches. Support them to notice how the number of the inches is large, but the number of feet is much smaller and thus easier to handle since the arithmetic is easier.

Other students may begin by using a repeated addition strategy, adding up 60 inches 6 times to get an overall total of 360 inches. This strategy works but it is cumbersome. Support them to consider how regrouping their groups might be more efficient. For example, they might consider how 6 groups of 60 is equivalent to 3 groups of 120 inches, or to 2 groups of 180 inches. Most likely if they produce 360 inches first without converting or using a model, they will try next to divide by 12 to determine the number of feet. Suggest that it might be easier to divide the 120 by 12 first, reminding them that mathematicians always look for efficiency. If they decide to go in this direction you can represent the partial quotients as 120/12 + 120/12 + 120/12 = 360/12. You can also build a bridge using these partial quotients to the standard algorithm, as shown in Figure 2.

$$
\begin{array}{r}
30 \\
12\overline{)360} \\
\end{array}
$$

120	10	120/12 + 120/12 + 120/12
240		= 360/12
120	10	
120		
120	10	

Figure 2: Bridging from partial quotients to the standard algorithm.

Finally, some students may try to convert everything to feet and then yards first, as the questions are listed in that order on the Appendix. Students can of course do the questions in any order they wish, and they should be encouraged to do so. However, the order was purposeful in that it could potentially suggest a strategy of converting first and using proportional reasoning, which the models also support: 60/12 = 5 feet, 180/12 = 15 feet, or 5 yards; hence 360/12 = 30 feet = 10 yards.

Behind the Numbers

The numbers have been chosen carefully to be supportive of the use of scaling. If students are comfortable with multiplication by ten, they will easily note that 120 inches is equal to 10 feet. Thus the sixth line, while representing 360 inches, also represents 30 feet, or 10 yards. Using these ratios eliminates a great deal of arithmetic. Although it also works to multiply 60 by 6 to get the total number of inches, and then to divide this product by 12 to determine the number of feet, or by 36 to determine the number of yards, there is a lot of arithmetic to do! And, there is also so much room to make calculation errors. Choosing numbers like these for the investigation ensures a variety of strategies and a rich discussion in the gallery walk and congress, which will be held on Day Two.

Inside One Classroom: Conferring with Students at Work

Catherine (the teacher): Hi Amy and Pauline. I've been looking at what you have been doing and I am fascinated by your strategy. Can I sit and confer with you on it?

Amy and Pauline: Sure! *(Both girls show genuine pleasure, beaming from the compliment.)*

Catherine: Well let me start by making sure I understand your strategy, OK? It looks to me like you are doing inches and feet first? You have written 60 inches = 5 feet, and when you got to the second line you wrote 120 inches and then you wrote 10 feet next to it? *(Both girls nod, so Catherine goes on, seeking more clarification.)* How did you know 120 inches would be 10 feet?

Author's notes

Catherine moves around the room, noting the strategies being used, and then sits to confer with a few groups as they work. She starts the conferral by clarifying what the

Amy: We skip counted. *(Pauline points to a line on their draft paper where they have made little ticks and written 12, 24, 36, 48, etc... up to 120.)*

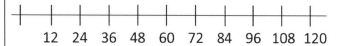

12 24 36 48 60 72 84 96 108 120

Catherine: Oh I see that now! And then you counted and found out it was 10 feet? *(The girls nod in agreement again, so Catherine continues.)* Wow! It is so helpful to model the problem isn't it! I wonder if this new model you made could also be helpful in figuring out how many yards there are.

Pauline: Maybe, ...the box says 3 feet in a yard. We could circle them on here...

Catherine: What a great idea! Go for it! Wow! You made such a powerful model! And now it is a tool for thinking! *(The girls have now made 3 circles with 3 feet in each, so Catherine continues.)* What will you do with this last foot?

Amy: We could just say 3 yards and 1 foot more.

Catherine: You could, but I'm also wondering if you know how much of a yard 1 foot is. Is it ½? There are 3 feet in a yard you said, right?

Pauline: No. It's smaller than the halfway mark. Three feet fit in a yard; not two.

Catherine: So if the yard is divided into 3 equal pieces to make a foot, then we could write it as 1/3. That means 1 divided by 3, and we call it one-third. Wow! You are inventing fractions! So are you saying 3 1/3 yards are equal to 10 feet?

Amy: *(pausing first, and then with exuberance)* We are! Right, Pauline?

Catherine: This is so exciting! You have to get this on your poster for our gallery walk tomorrow! Do you think you can now continue like this to figure out how long the whole line is in yards? I'll check back with you later and you can let me know, ok?

children have done. Before she sat down she already had a good idea of the strategy they were using.

Catherine notes the power of starting with a model. This can go a long way in helping kids develop a growth mindset and the willingness to persevere—one of the important standards of mathematical practice. Then she supports by celebrating the strategy and challenging them to use it to do yards. This move "ups the ante," but in a very supportive way. The role of the teacher is not to just facilitate; it is to mentor.

Catherine does not hold back in helping the girls see that 1 yard divided into 3 equal pieces is written as 1/3, and she explains that the notation means 1 divided by 3. The notation is social knowledge and can be told as long as the girls understand that it represents what they said: 1 yard has 3 equal feet in it.

As she leaves to confer with other pairs at work, Catherine urges the girls to make sure they get that idea on their poster. This idea will be an important focus in the congress tomorrow.

As students begin to reach conclusions about how long the line is, ask them to prepare posters presenting their findings for a gallery walk and congress on Day Two. Explain that mathematicians often want to share their findings with each other, and that when they do they are careful to choose the most important ideas to share. As students prepare their work on poster paper, they should not copy every step they took. Instead, encourage students to record how their thinking changed, the interesting connections they noticed, and the arguments they used to convince each other that their answers were correct. How did they convert from inches to feet and to yards? Did they do the feet first, and then the yards, or the reverse? Why? What did they notice along the way that might have made their work easier?

Reflections on the Day

Today students were asked to measure length and to convert between inches, yards, and feet. The double number line (which emerged as a representation of Patricio's measuring with a tape measure) can be used as a helpful tool in converting from one unit to another. The model supports the use of ratio thinking and using it saves a lot of arithmetic! It also supports children to use multiplicative structuring instead of additive structuring. Along the way students most likely came to realize that as the unit used became bigger, the number of times they needed to iterate it was proportionately smaller. Day Two's congress will provide an opportunity for a rich discussion about ways to convert from one unit to another and how using larger units makes the numbers smaller and can require far less work!

DAY TWO

WHICH LENGTH?

Materials Needed

Students' work from Day One

Markers and Pencils

Sticky notes (about 3 per student)

Today begins with a minilesson as a warm-up to math workshop. Students work with a string of related problems designed to support further ratio thinking in converting from one unit to another. After the minilesson, finishing touches are put to posters and a gallery walk ensues to provide students with opportunities to read and write viable arguments—an important standard of mathematical practice. After the gallery walk a congress is held to discuss a few of the pieces more deeply.

Day Two Outline

Minilesson: A String of Related Problems

❖ Work on a string of related problems designed to encourage students to convert fluently using multiplicative structuring.

Facilitating the Gallery Walk

❖ Confer with children as they put finishing touches to their posters, asking them to consider the most important things they want to tell their audience about smart ways to convert.

❖ Conduct a gallery walk to allow students time to reflect and comment on each other's posters from Day One.

Facilitating the Math Congress

❖ Convene students at the meeting area to discuss a few important ideas about converting from one unit of measure to another, such as the fact that the bigger the unit used the fewer iterations needed. Examine how some strategies required a great deal of arithmetic while others didn't.

Minilesson: A String of Related Problems

This string is designed to help students use multiplicative structuring, more flexibly converting one unit to another using strategies based on ratio thinking. Represent the problems on a t-chart like the one below, one problem at a time, moving from the top to the bottom of the chart, and invite students to share their conversion strategies. As they do, record their thinking on the t-chart.

The String:

	Inches	Feet	Yards
12 inches	12		
2 feet		2	
1 yard			1
2 yards			2
4 yards			4
10 feet		10	
5 feet		5	
8 yards			8

Behind the Numbers

The first problem is a helper requiring only the knowledge given the day before: 12 inches equals 1 foot. The yard will be a challenge as it is only a fractional part: 1/3 of a yard. You can support children to see this by drawing an open number line and marking three equal parts on it. If you have a yard and three rulers, you can demonstrate with those. As you move through the string many relations will surface such as doubling, halving, and partial products. Encourage children to note the relations and use them to convert.

Facilitating the Gallery Walk

Ask students to return to the posters they began on Day One, adding any finishing touches they desire. As they work, move around and confer asking them to consider the most important things they want to tell their audience about smart ways to convert. Remind them that it is not necessary to write about everything they did, but instead to concentrate on convincing their audience about the important things they discovered and want to defend. Depending on how much prior experience your students have had doing gallery walks, it may be helpful to provide instructions before you pass out the sticky notes. If your students have not done a gallery walk for some time, or if you think they need more instruction on how to proceed, see the Teacher Note section below.

Teacher Note

Let your students know that their comments and questions should be specific about the math on the poster, and to steer clear of comments such as "Good job!" or "I like your poster." Remind students that mathematicians write proofs. They defend their ideas to convince other mathematicians that they are right. Thus, specific comments and questions are most helpful. It may help to give the example of writing workshop, since most students can remember a time when a peer said something like, "I like your story!" but did not explain why. Once you have gone over a few examples and perhaps even modeled writing a comment or question, pass out the sticky notes. Explain that you are going to start by passing out three sticky notes, and students can return to get more if needed.

Ask students to start at different places and choose three or four posters to focus on. Remind them to read carefully and then give each poster a few sticky notes, enough so that after about ten minutes, all posters will have at least a few comments. Remind students that gallery walks should be quiet times so that all reviewers can read and think before commenting. This time should be taken seriously. One of the Standards of Mathematical Practice is to read and write viable arguments and this is a time to foster the development of that ability.

After the gallery walk, invite the groups to go back to their posters to see what comments and questions were left. Allow a few minutes for everyone to think about the feedback they received and to discuss any new ideas with their partners before convening the whole class in the meeting area for a congress.

Facilitating the Congress

Review the posters and choose a few that you can use for a discussion that will deepen understanding and support growth along the landscape of learning described in the overview. There is not necessarily one best plan for a congress. There are many different plans that might all be supportive of development.

If your school has purchased P2S2™, the support system for CFLM (www.NewPerspectivesOnline.net), you will find many tips on it about how to plan congresses. For example, you might start with a sample pair that used skip counting or repeated addition (an example of additive structuring), tediously working to get a total of the number of inches first. If they used a model and then circled the number of feet and yards on it, it might serve as a nice piece to discuss the power of drawing a model and using it as a tool. Starting the congress with a piece like this will also serve as a support for other students who may have found multiplicative structuring and the use of ratio thinking difficult.

A second nice choice might be a piece by a pair that started by converting first: 60 inches into 5 feet; 120 inches into 10 feet; 180 into 15 feet; etc. Here you can ask everyone to step back and look for any patterns in the numbers that they might see. Support them to notice that the inches are going up by sixties and the feet are going up by fives. If they notice that every other tick has numbers with zeroes at the end you might represent on a t-chart, as you did with the minilesson, and remove the zeroes, writing 12 inches = 1 foot; 120 inches = 10 feet; 24 inches = 2 feet; and 240 inches = 20 feet, etc. Encourage discussion on the relation between 12 inches and 120 inches and 1 foot and 10 feet to promote scaling.

A third nice choice might be a poster that shows the use of yards, for example noting that 120 inches is 10 feet, and therefore the entire length is 30 feet, which divided by 3 produces 10 yards. Thinking like this is a beautiful example of multiplicative structuring because of the flexible scaling up and scaling down using proportional reasoning.

Whatever pieces you decide to use, make sure that one of the big ideas discussed is that the bigger the units used when measuring, the smaller the number of iterations. Using yards produces an answer of 10, whereas using feet produces a length of 30, and using inches produces an answer of 360. Promote discussion on how all are correct. Since a yard is 3 times as big as a foot, the answer is 3 times smaller than the total number of feet, but the measurements are equivalent.

Reflections on the Day

Math workshop began today with a minilesson where students were supported to convert making use of the relationships in a t-chart. The minilesson may have supported your students to refine their thinking as they prepared for the gallery walk. By participating in a gallery walk on their work from Day One, students had opportunities to read and write viable arguments and then consider their classmates' comments, questions, and suggestions. Opportunities like these are designed to support the development of proof-making. A math congress provided opportunities for further discussion and reflection on the topic of measurement conversion and by the end of the day you are likely already noticing how several of your students are starting to think proportionally.

DAY THREE

PATRICIO'S MODEL

Materials Needed	

Patricio's Model
(Appendix C, one
copy per pair of
students)

Pencils

**Drawing paper or
several sheets of
copy paper**

**Blank Chart Paper for
posters** (sticky note
style is best as it
makes taping on the
walls unnecessary)

Markers

Today begins with a minilesson as a warm-up to math workshop. Students work with a string of related problems designed to support further ratio thinking in converting from one unit to another. After the minilesson a new context is presented. The line has gotten so long that customers are complaining and want to know how long they will have to wait. Patricio has a new mystery to solve. He needs to put up some signs so customers can tell how long the wait is as they are standing in line. How can he figure this out, and what should he put on the signs: seconds, minutes, or hours?

Day Three Outline

Minilesson: A String of Related Problems
❖ Work on a string of related problems designed to encourage students to convert fluently using multiplicative structuring.

Developing the Context
❖ Tell the story of Patricio's Experiment using Appendix C.
❖ Facilitate a discussion on how Patricio's model might be helpful and ask students to finish it.
❖ Send students off in pairs to figure out the length of the new line in yards, feet, and inches and how long it will take for the last customer at the end to get to the counter.

Supporting the Investigation
❖ Confer with children as they work, noting the strategies they use and how they convert.
❖ As students finish, ask them to prepare a poster to convince others of their solutions and important things they have noticed along the way as they worked. These posters will be used on Day Four in a gallery walk and congress.

Minilesson: A String of Related Problems

This string is designed in a similar fashion to the one you used on Day Two. Its purpose is to help students use multiplicative structuring to convert more flexibly from one unit to another, using strategies based on ratio thinking. Represent the problems on a t-chart like the one below, one problem at a time, moving from the top to the bottom of the chart, and invite students to share their conversion strategies. As they do, record their thinking on the t-chart.

The String:

Inches	Feet	Yards
		1
		2
		3
		9
		10
		5
		19

Behind the Numbers

The first problem is a helper requiring only the knowledge given the day before: 1 yard equals 3 feet. Calculating the inches is just 3x12=36, which most children should easily be able to do with skip counting or with the partial products of 30 + 6. Two yards is double, so the inches and the feet double: 72 inches, or 6 feet. To determine 3 yards, 1 yard and 2 yards can be combined, or 1 yard can be tripled. 9 yards is a triple of 3 yards (27 feet) and 10 is just one yard more (30 feet) or ten times the first set of measurements on the table. 5 yards is half of 10 so the feet and inches are halved as well. 19 may be difficult for some but encourage them to look for pieces they know, for example 10 and 9 can be added to produce partial products of 360 + 324 = 684 inches, or 30 + 27 = 57 feet. Both partial products and scaling can be supported with this string.

Developing the Context

Project a copy of Appendix C if you have the technology to do so, and read the story on it as you develop the context. If you don't have the technology, just pass out Appendix C so that each pair of students has a copy and read the story on it to them. Remember to develop it in an exciting way to engage them in the story. Make the context come alive!

Discuss the context to make sure students understand Patricio's experiment and his model, also ensuring they understand that Patricio used a longer tape measure than before. Ask if students think this was helpful. Was Patricio right when he thought that if he used a longer tool there would be less work? You might ask them to consider if he had used the smaller tape measure: would he have still had 6 marks?

Some students will likely comment that some customers might take longer and Patricio can't assume that every 10 minutes 6 people will get to the counter. Of course this is true. Acknowledge that it is a good point, but remind students of the situation. Patricio needs to place signs that show average times so customers can judge whether they want to wait or not. Point out that the first group of 6 people that took 10 minutes might have had some customers who were quick and others who took longer, too. You can also say that often mathematicians have to decide ahead on certain assumptions they will use when they set out to mathematize a problem. As a community it is important to use the same assumptions or it is difficult to compare solutions. Patricio's model assumes 120 inches for 6 people and that takes about 10 minutes. Suggest that as a community this rate be the one used to finish Patricio's model, since it is the rate he started with, then send them off in pairs to finish the model and work on the questions on Appendix C. Remind students that they have drawing paper, too, if they want to redraw the model to help them.

Supporting the Investigation

The drawing of the line with the marks and a ratio table are provided again on purpose as they may potentially generate a strategy of proportional reasoning. For example, some students might write 120 inches under the first line and then convert to feet first, noting above the line the equivalence of 10 feet every 10 minutes. If they do this they now have a nice ratio they can use: if 120 inches is equivalent to 10 feet, and this takes 10 minutes, then if there are 6 marks it will take an hour (6 x 10 minutes) for the last customer to get to the counter.

Others may use 10 minutes for 10 feet and scale down first, establishing a rate of a foot a minute. If the first tape measure (Day One, 60 inches) had 6 marks and that was 30 feet, or 10 yards, and now this bigger tape measure is twice as long but also has 6 marks, the total distance of this new line must be twice as long. So, it would be 60 feet (or 20 yards). If every foot takes a minute, then it will take an hour (60 minutes, or 3,600 seconds) for the last customer to get to the counter.

Some students may calculate the number of people first: 6 people in each group and 6 groups since there are 6 marks. This means there are 36 people in line. If 6 people (1 group) take 10 minutes, it will take 60 minutes for the last of the 36 people to get to the counter. This is another example of scaling both 6 and 10 up by 6.

There are many strategies that can be used to solve the problem and Patricio's model should be a helpful one to support movement from skip counting and/or tedious arithmetic strategies to the use of scaling. Confer with children as they work, noting the strategies they use as they scale up and convert. Do they add, skip count, or use partial products? Do they think about why with different tape measures there were still 6 marks? As you confer support students to use more flexible strategies than they used on Day One and celebrate with them the advances you see in their approaches.

Some students may represent the minutes as a portion of an hour in a variety of ways and as you confer keep an eye out for this. For example, take a look at the samples of work in Figure 3. The first piece makes no attempt to show the minutes as a portion of the whole hour. It is important to get your students to consider what portion of the hour 10 minutes is. It is true there is not a complete hour yet, but there is a portion of an hour. Encourage students to examine how many 10-minute portions there are in an hour and establish the equivalence: 10 minutes = 1/6 of an hour. This is the thinking that is evident in the third sample. It represents thinking of the 10 minutes as 1 part out of 6 parts: 10 minutes x 6 = 60 minutes. Note how the second piece of work attempts to show the minutes using decimal notation. Students will often do this so keep a look out for it. They are not considering the decimals as ratios representing a portion of the whole broken into hundredths. The hour does not have 100 minutes in it, only 60, so ten minutes is 10/60 of an hour, not 10/100.

minutes	seconds	hours	people
10	600	0	6
20	1,200	0	12
30	1,800	0	18
40	2,400	0	24
50	3,000	0	30
60	3,600	1	36

10min 10min 10min 10min

minutes	seconds	hours	people
10	600	0.10 min	6
20	1,200	0.20 min	12
30	1,800	0.30 min	18
40	2,400	0.40 min	24
50	3,000	0.50 min	30
60	3,600	1 hour	36

minutes	seconds	hours	people
10	600		6
20	1,200		12
30	1,800		18
40	2,400		24
50	3,000		30
60	3,600		36
70	4,200		42

Figure 3: Three Samples of Student Work

As students finish, ask them to prepare a poster to convince others of their solutions and important things they have noticed along the way as they worked. These posters will be used on Day Four in a gallery walk and congress.

Reflections on the Day

Math workshop today again began with a minilesson where students were supported to convert making use of the relationships in a t-chart. The minilesson may have supported your students to make use of scaling and partial products and you may have seen these strategies carrying over when students worked on Patricio's model. As you moved around and conferred you may have noticed also that more and more students are starting to use ratio thinking. The movement from skip counting to scaling is huge as it requires a shift from additive structuring to multiplicative structuring—to thinking proportionally. You are witnessing major development in front of your eyes and it is important to document it. Take a look at the landscape in the overview. Have you seen your children traversing the landscape? Continue to document each child's journey along it. You can highlight each child's path on the graphic of the landscape provided in the overview of this unit. There is an app available to do so as well if you wish to capture and document your students' development digitally (www.NewPerspectivesOnAssessment.com).

DAY FOUR

HOW LONG A WAIT?

Materials Needed

Students' work from Day Three

Markers

Sticky notes (about 3 per student)

Today begins with students adding finishing touches to posters from Day Three and a gallery walk ensues. After the gallery walk a congress is held to discuss a few of the pieces more deeply. The congress ends with a minilesson. Students work with a string of related problems designed to support further ratio thinking in converting from one unit to another.

Day Four Outline

Facilitating the Gallery Walk

❖ Confer with children as they put finishing touches to their posters, asking them to consider the most important things they want to tell their audience about smart ways to convert.

❖ Conduct a gallery walk to allow students time to reflect and comment on each other's posters.

Facilitating the Math Congress

❖ Convene students at the meeting area to discuss a few important ideas about converting from one unit of measure to another, such as how Patricio's model might have been helpful and how it might not have been necessary to calculate each mark to know how long it would take.

Minilesson: A String of Related Problems

❖ Work on a string of related problems designed to encourage students to convert fluently using multiplicative structuring.

Facilitating the Gallery Walk

Ask students to return to the posters they began on Day Three, adding any finishing touches they desire. As they work, move around and confer, asking them to consider the most important things they want to tell their audience about smart ways to convert. Remind them that it is not necessary to write about everything they did, but instead to concentrate on convincing their audience about the important things they discovered and want to defend.

The main purpose of a Gallery Walk is of course the development of the reading and writing of viable arguments, but a secondary purpose is to provide time for reflection, refinement, and consolidation of the thinking learners generated as they investigated the problem. Often when students are postering, the ideas they write about go beyond what they actually did. Students may have started with just skip counting strategies or doing a great deal of arithmetic, but as they worked they might have had an insight on a more efficient strategy. In particular they may have moved from additive structuring to a more multiplicative way of thinking, for example doubling or scaling. They should focus their posters on this second strategy, as it represents an insight they had that is an important idea to share. Encouraging students to just write about what they did may not be as supportive of development as encouraging them to write about an insight they had as they worked and to write a convincing argument about it. As you move around conferring and helping your students to get ready for the gallery walk, look for moments where you can facilitate development—moments where you can support scaling and other more efficient strategies.

Ask students to start at different places and choose three or four posters to focus on. Remind them to read carefully and then give each poster a few sticky notes, enough so that after about ten minutes, all posters will have at least a few comments. Remind students that gallery walks should be quiet times so that all reviewers can read and think before commenting. This time should be taken seriously.

Facilitating the Math Congress

Review the posters and choose a few that you can use for a discussion that will deepen understanding and support growth along the landscape of learning described in the overview. There is not necessarily one best plan for a congress. There are many different plans that might all be supportive of development.

Tech Tip

You might take pictures of students' work using an iPad and project them onto a whiteboard or smart board. When different ideas come up in discussions, revisions can be drawn without having to mark on the student's work. Apps such as *Adobe Sketch* or *Explain Everything* can be useful tools for this.

You'll want to make this congress supportive of the use of the ratio table as a tool: jumping around the table in clever ways for converting and using equivalent rates. But remember to work developmentally. If you start with an approach that shows a strong understanding of scaling, for example, but one that will be difficult for most of your students to understand, you will lose many during the discussion. Think about how to scaffold your congress so that entry levels exist for those who aren't thinking multiplicatively yet. Think about how you might connect the strategies you use so that the discussion that occurs actually promotes new insights. A window into one classroom follows as an example.

Inside One Classroom: A Portion of the Congress

Catherine (the teacher): Yesterday we started math workshop with a minilesson and discussed how some problems could be helpful with others. I noticed during our gallery walk how many of you found interesting ways to calculate the time by doing just that. And different people used different points on Patricio's model. Let's look at a few together and let's see what we came up with. Sally and Ben, would you start us off and explain your approach?

Sally: Well, we noticed that the tape measure that Patricio got from the carpenter was twice as big as the one he used earlier, so we doubled everything.

Ben: Yeah. See...we marked a make-believe mark in the middle of each of the marks on Patricio's model. Before it was 60 inches so we put that in the middle, but really it is 120 and that is 10 feet, so we made that second mark darker. And then we just went 10, 20, 30, 40, 50, 60 at each dark mark, the ones on Patricio's model.

Catherine: Interesting! Let's turn and talk with a shoulder partner. See if your partner knows what Ben and Sally did. *(After a few minutes of pair talk, Catherine resumes whole group discussion.)* Who has a question or comment for Ben and Sally?

Noah: How did you know what numbers to put with the tens? I know it is 120 inches for 10 feet, but how did you know the others?

Author's notes

Catherine starts the congress with a piece of work that makes use of doubling. For children who still need to mark each line, for example those that are still skip counting, it provides an entry point. Using doubles to scale is the beginning of multiplicative structuring. Some children may not as of yet be able to see where the more generalized scaling comes from, as that requires a deep understanding of equivalent rates and proportional reasoning, but they can often see the doubling.

Pair talk is provided to discuss what the group has done and to give time to reflect on it. Discussion is not possible without the majority of the group understanding the strategy. The pair talk supports others to now ask questions. It is important to get the conversation going back and forth between the students rather than teacher/kid/teacher.

Ben: They were just doubles from the other day because 120 is double of 60. First we did every other one and marked the sixties in between but then we realized we didn't need them. The answer was just a double of the other day.

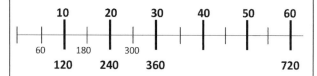

Noah: Oh, I get it! It's just like the other day, except everything is double! But then how did you figure out the time?

Sally: That's the part we got really excited by! We realized the top of our line wasn't just the feet. It was the minutes, too! Every 10 minutes it was 10 feet….so it took an hour for the last customer to get to the counter. Those must be good truffles! I wouldn't have waited that long!

Children: Yes! Too long to wait!

Catherine: *(smiling at their humor)* Eva and Sophie, let's post your work up next. Your strategy is very similar to Ben and Sally's but you had even fewer steps. You stopped at the first mark! What did you do to get the answer?

Eva: We thought of 10 feet sort of like a clock too….and we knew there were 6 pieces, so we did 6 x 10 minutes to get 60 minutes. And then we did 6 x 120 inches to get 720 inches. At first we couldn't figure out how to do the yards but then we realized we knew it was 10 yards for 360 minutes, so we doubled and got 20 yards for 720 inches.

Catherine: Who agrees? *(Lots of hands go up.)* Turn and explain it to your partner. See if they need help understanding it.

Now Ben's explanation makes more sense. And the community is being requested to consider early scaling, which was Catherine's goal.

Eva and Sophie have used a more sophisticated version of proportional reasoning and if Catherine had started with this piece, several students in the class would have been lost. Now it is more accessible because it can be connected to the first piece of work that Ben and Sally explained.

Minilesson: A String of Related Problems

This string is designed to continue helping students use multiplicative structuring, more flexibly converting one unit to another using strategies based on ratio thinking. Doing it after the congress instead of at the beginning of math workshop is beneficial because the congress supported the ability to scale and this gives students a chance to practice what they were discussing.

Represent the problems on a t-chart like the one below, one problem at a time, moving from the top to the bottom of the chart, and invite students to share their conversion strategies. As they do, record their thinking on the t-chart.

The String:

1 foot
2 feet
5 feet
240 inches
40 minutes
22 feet
19 feet
1 hour

Inches	Feet	Time in Minutes
120	10	10
	1	
	2	
	5	
240		
		40
	22	
	19	
		1 hour

Reflections on the Day

Math workshop began today with preparation for a gallery walk. As you moved around and conferred you may have noticed that more and more students are now starting to use ratio thinking. Each day you should see your children making progress on the landscape, but each child's pathway will likely be different. The lessons are not designed with one goal for all—one "it" for everyone to get. Each child should be learning, but most likely they are not all learning the same thing. Learning *is* development. The movement from skip counting to scaling is huge as it requires a shift from additive structuring to multiplicative structuring—to thinking proportionally. You are witnessing major development in front of your eyes. Document the journey!

DAY FIVE

MUFFLES' RECIPES

Today begins with another minilesson designed to support multiplicative structuring and the flexible conversion of units of time. Then a new context is developed. Muffles' shop has become so popular he needs to make bigger batches of his truffles in order to have enough each day for his long lines of customers. In this investigation students are introduced to some new units: cups, pints, quarts, and gallons and ounces and pounds. This context also uses a ratio table as a tool to support further scaling up and down. As students work to generate recipes for larger batches, many opportunities will occur for rich discussions on equivalence and proportional reasoning related to measurement.

Day Five Outline

Minilesson: A String of Related Problems
❖ Work on a string of related time problems designed to encourage students to convert fluently using multiplicative structuring.

Developing the Context
❖ Tell the story of Muffles' recipes and the units of measure he uses in making his truffles using Appendix E.
❖ Facilitate a discussion on the equivalence of the units shown on Appendix D.
❖ Ask students to work in pairs on Appendix E, making a recipe chart for various batches of Muffles' dark chocolate truffles.

Supporting the Investigation
❖ Confer with children as they work, noting the strategies they use and how they convert.
❖ As students finish, ask them to prepare a poster to convince others of their solutions and important things they have noticed along the way as they worked. These posters will be used on Day Six in a gallery walk and congress.

Minilesson: A String of Related Problems

This string is designed in a similar fashion to the others you have been using all week. Its purpose, as with the others, is to keep familiarizing students with conversions. The focus today is on time. It also helps students use multiplicative structuring to convert more flexibly from one unit to another, using strategies based on proportional reasoning. Represent the problems on a t-chart like the one below, showing only one problem at a time, moving from the top to the bottom of the chart, and invite students to share their conversion strategies. As they do, record their thinking on the t-chart.

The String:

Seconds	Minutes	Hours
3600	60	1
		10
		2
		5
		9
		11
		6

Behind the Numbers

As students work to convert hours into seconds, the numbers will quickly become large. That is purposeful. The unwieldiness of trying to multiply each problem separately will cause students to consider the beauty of using other problems in the string and using strategies based on proportional reasoning. The first problem is a helper requiring only the knowledge given before: 1 hour = 60 minutes = 3600 seconds. The numbers are related in interesting ways to support the use of scaling and using partial products. As you work through the string you might not require students to do all of the arithmetic. Let them just tell you the strategies they would use so you can focus discussion on the relationships they see. For example, 9 hours can be solved as 600-60 minutes, and as 36,000-3,600 seconds. If you want to do the arithmetic together, use an open number line model and remove helpful pieces: 36,000 − 3,000 − 600 = 32,400.

Developing the Context

Use Appendices D and E as you tell the following story. Remember to make the context come alive!

> *The line of customers at the shop keeps getting longer and longer and Patricio is kept very busy making signs to let customers know the approximate wait time. And, as you can imagine, Muffles is kept very busy making batch after batch of his famous truffles.*

Muffles finally decides he has to make bigger batches, at least for his most popular and best-selling types of truffles. He looks over his basic recipe, which makes 60 dark chocolate truffles, and he thinks to himself, "I'll double it, ...no, I better triple it, or maybe quadruple it! A batch 4 times as big! Wow! I might even make really big batches! And, I'll make big charts for my new recipes to hang in the kitchen so my assistants can make the truffles when I'm not here."

Point out to the children that the basic recipe is in ounces and cups but as Muffles makes bigger batches he might want to use different units of measure to save time. Introduce the units listed on Appendix D, helping your students to understand the equivalences: 1 pound = 16 ounces; 2 cups = 1 pint; 2 pints = 1 quart; and 4 quarts = 1 gallon.

Assign math partners and send students off to investigate what Muffles should write on his new charts.

Teacher Note: Behind the Numbers

The basic recipe proportions come from a standard truffles recipe. However, note that the basic recipe uses ounces and cups. As larger batches are made it makes more sense to measure with larger containers (units) and this provides students with the challenge of how best to convert. Samples of children's work from field testing are provided in *Supporting the Investigation* to help you anticipate what your children might do.

Supporting the Investigation

As you move around conferring, take note of how children are moving on the table. Often, many students go across the top row first and when they get to the Very Big Batch they just assign a scaling factor randomly (for example 10 times the Big Batch, or 100 times the Basic Recipe, or 60 times the Big Batch perhaps from their work with the clock on Day Four). They also don't scale each ingredient by the same factor as they go down a column. For an example, see the work sample in Figure 4.1.

As you confer with students who do this, query them on why they picked the numbers they did. Suggest that they check the 1 gallon of milk since it is on Muffles' chart already and see how many cups there are in one gallon. Ask what the relationship of the gallon is to the cup in the Basic Recipe. Stay grounded in the context. You might say, "If we only double the chocolate but use ten times the amount of milk would the batch be as chocolatey? When you make chocolate milk if you don't put much chocolate in the milk what happens?" For an example of how to confer on this see the dialogue box from Inside One Classroom on page 36.

Other children may scale consistently and may convert from smaller units to bigger ones as the quantities increase. Figure 4.2 shows an example of flexible scaling and converting.

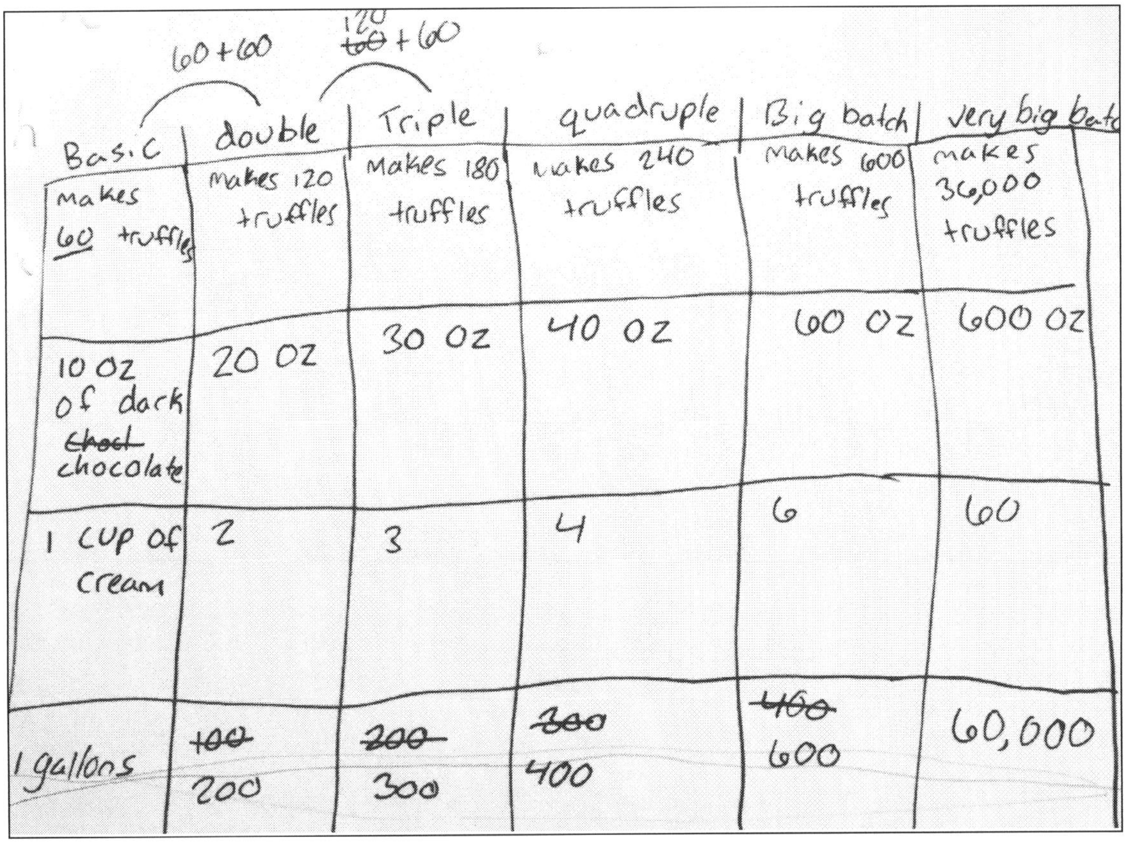

Basic	double	Triple	quadruple	Big batch	very big batch
makes 60 truffles	makes 120 truffles	makes 180 truffles	makes 240 truffles	makes 600 truffles	makes 36,000 truffles
10 oz of dark ~~choc~~ chocolate	20 oz	30 oz	40 oz	60 oz	600 oz
1 cup of cream	2	3	4	6	60
1 gallons	~~100~~ 200	~~200~~ 300	~~300~~ 400	~~400~~ 600	60,000

60+60   ~~120~~ 100+60

Figure 4.1: Randomly choosing numbers to scale by

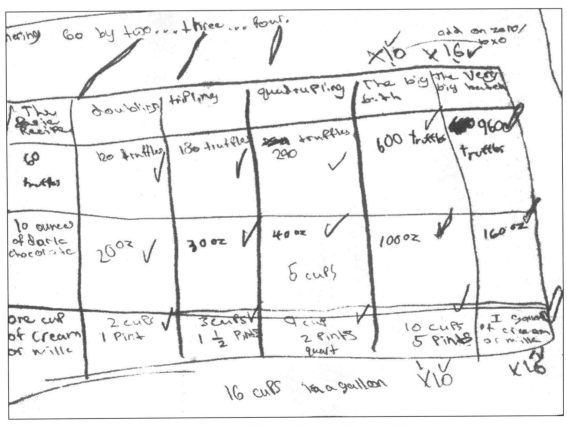

Figure 4.2: Flexible scaling and conversions

Catherine (the teacher): How are the three of you doing? May I sit and confer with you? *(The students all nod affirmatively and so Catherine continues.)* I see that you have written 36,000 truffles for the Very Big Batch. How did you get that number?

Josie: We multiplied the Big Batch by 600. See we wrote it down here. *(On their paper they have written 600 x 60 = 36,000.)*

Catherine: Yes, I see that now. But why 600? What made you decide to multiply by 600? Did you think this batch was 600 times bigger than the Basic Recipe? That's a lot of truffles! And I see that you then multiplied 1 cup of cream in the Basic Recipe by 60. I'm confused. How would you get 36,000 truffles, which you said was 600 times the Basic Recipe, if you only do 60 cups of the cream? I'm also puzzled because it says 1 gallon of cream for the Very Big Batch. Does one gallon have 60 cups in it? Whew!! This is a real mystery, isn't it?

Josh: We could check the cups...

Catherine: What a great idea! Go for it!

Josh: The Basic had 1 cup, so the double had 2 cups.

Catherine: I wonder if it would be helpful here to convert to pints. Remember on the other days how the bigger measurement units made the arithmetic easier because the numbers got smaller? I'm not sure, but it might help. What do you think?

Sasha: 2 cups is a pint. We could write that.

Catherine: You could even write both and then see what helps the most. How much milk does Muffles need when he triples and quadruples the Basic Recipe?

Sasha: When he triples he needs 3 cups and then 4 cups when he quadruples.

Josie: 4 cups is 2 pints. I just doubled the 2.

Josh: *(looking at Appendix D)* And, 4 cups is 1 quart, and there are 4 quarts in a gallon.

Catherine: This is so exciting! I think we've cracked part of the mystery! So the Very Big Batch is only 4 times bigger than the quadrupled batch?

Author's notes

Catherine starts the conferral by clarifying what the children have done. Before she sat down she already had a good idea of the strategy they were using and she seeks in her next move to create disequilibrium. Intrigue can go a long way in helping kids develop the willingness to persevere—one of the important standards of mathematical practice. Then she supports by celebrating their next move.

Suggesting that they convert is a way of reminding them of one of the big ideas in this unit: the larger the unit of measure, the smaller the total—and this makes the arithmetic easier.

Once again a celebration occurs. Note how it also feels to the children that Catherine is engaging in the inquiry with them. She even uses the pronoun "we." It's a conversation as she confers. It's not a test about what they know and where they made a mistake.

Sasha: Oh yeah! Because if you mixed up 4 quadruple batches you'd have 4 quarts and that's a gallon worth of milk.

Catherine: You have to get this on your poster for our gallery walk tomorrow! So if Muffles needed 40 ounces of chocolate for the quadrupled batch and the Very Big Batch is 4 times bigger, how many ounces of chocolate would he need? And, if he made 240 truffles with the quadrupled recipe I wonder how many truffles he will get with the Very Big Batch. I want to keep working with you, but I need to get to some other groups, too. I'll check back with you later and you can let me know, ok?

As she leaves to confer with other pairs at work, Catherine urges the trio to make sure they get that idea on their poster. This idea will be an important focus in the congress tomorrow.

Reflections on the Day

Math workshop began today with another minilesson. Are the minilessons causing children to look for relationships and use them? If so, that is wonderful as they are making use of partial products and scaling. If not, reflect on how you might scaffold this more clearly during the discussion or perhaps repeat a string with a smaller group of children to allow everyone more space to reflect and be accountable for new ideas.

Remember that you can document children's growth on the landscape. You can jot down notes from the discussion after class and record your evidence on the landscape. And, even when this unit ends you can keep doing minilessons every day to continue working on multiplicative structuring and measurement conversions and record children's further progress. The investigation today was designed to introduce more units of measurement: this time for weight and liquid volume. As you moved around and conferred you may have noticed some children not scaling proportionately. Did you stay grounded in the context to help them? Did you find yourself asking "If we only double the chocolate but use ten times the amount of milk would the batch be as chocolatey?" Context will help children come to realize what they are doing. Without it, they can get lost in a world of numbers and have nothing to hang their hat on!

DAY SIX

MUFFLES' DARK CHOCOLATE TRUFFLES

Materials Needed

Students' work from Day Five

Sticky notes (approximately 3 per student)

Today begins with students adding finishing touches to posters from Day Five and a gallery walk ensues. After the gallery walk a congress is held to discuss the relationship between the batches, the need to scale by the same factor, and the way the numbers change when they convert between different units of weight and volume. The congress ends with a minilesson. Students work with a string of related problems designed to support further ratio thinking in converting from one measurement unit to another.

Day Six Outline

Facilitating the Gallery Walk

❖ Confer with children as they put finishing touches to their posters, asking them to consider the most important things they want to tell their audience about smart ways to convert.

❖ Conduct a gallery walk to allow students time to reflect and comment on each other's posters on the investigation started on Day Five.

Facilitating the Math Congress

❖ Convene students at the meeting area to discuss a few important ideas about converting efficiently from one unit of measure to another.

Minilesson: A String of Related Problems

❖ Work on a string of related problems designed to encourage students to convert fluently using multiplicative structuring.

Facilitating the Gallery Walk

Ask students to return to the posters they began on Day Five, adding any finishing touches they desire. As they work, move around and confer, asking them to consider the most important things they want to tell their audience about smart ways to convert. Remind them that it is not necessary to write about everything they did, but instead to concentrate on convincing their audience about the important things they discovered and want to defend.

Remember that during the gallery walk it's important that you make comments on posters as well. It's important that students see you as a member of the community, so look for moments and places where you can show them you are seriously trying to understand their thinking. Make your comments as a member of the audience, suggesting where more detail could be helpful to support understanding and commenting on interesting approaches. Raise questions that might push for generalization. As you move around look for big ideas and strategies from the landscape. This is a nice time to also plan which pieces of work you will select for the congress.

Facilitating the Math Congress

Review the posters and choose a few that you can use for a discussion that will deepen understanding and support growth along the landscape of learning described in the overview. There is not necessarily one best plan for a congress. There are many different plans that might all be supportive of development. The dialogue box below presents a portion of a congress designed to help students who are doubling and halving develop a more generalized strategy for scaling.

Inside One Classroom: A Portion of the Congress

Catherine (the teacher) brings up the group she spoke with on Day Five who had to go back and re-calculate with a consistent scale factor.

Catherine: Josie, Josh, and Sasha I've got a picture of your work up on the projector here. You had to work really hard on the Very Big Batch didn't you? Please come up and tell us how you figured out what to do.

Sasha: Well at first we just knew that the numbers had to be very big, so we used big ones. But then we realized that our batch might end up too milky or too dry if we weren't careful.

Josie: 1 gallon was the clue. You told us that the milk had to be one gallon, because Muffles had already written that in.

Josh: So then we checked the cups and after everything it adds up to 16 cups in a gallon.

Author's notes

Catherine starts with a group who has made significant progress during this investigation, knowing that their evolution of thinking will help other students find similar insights.

Catherine: Did you really use addition to get up to 16?

Josh: Oh no, you're right. We doubled up to pints and then doubled to quarts and quadrupled to gallons, so that's…. multiplying.

Sasha: And we already had a batch with a quart, so we just did that one times 4 since it was 4 quarts in a gallon. So that's how we got 960 truffles and 160 ounces.

Catherine: So you used the relationship with the units to help you convert? That's helpful! And once you knew you were going from the one quart to four, you knew you had to quadruple everything?

Sasha: Yes. I don't even know why we did the 16 cups, actually. That wasn't helpful.

Catherine: You know, it's interesting that you say that. Because I also saw another group that did use 16. Talia and Aidan, can you come up and explain what you did?

Talia: Well, we always went up from the basic batch. Each new batch had a hint like Josie was saying that told you what it had to be.

Aidan: So for the Big Batch we knew that 60 to 600 had to be times 10, and we did times 10 for the chocolate and the milk too.

Catherine: So you did all the pieces of the recipe times 10 at once? Was that important?

Aidan: Yeah, you have to do that to keep the balance. With "tripling" and "quadrupling" it says it in the words, but there isn't a word for times-tensing. But it's the same idea.

Sasha: Tentupling?

Aidan: Yeah!

Talia: And then we 16-tupled, or whatever. We did all the things times 16 and we got 1 gallon, 960 truffles, and 160 ounces just like the other group.

Catherine: Whoa! I'm hearing a lot here. So there were a couple of different ways we could multiply up get to the very big batch on this ratio table, huh? Did anyone else see a different relationship we could use for the 1 gallon clue?

Catherine wants to emphasize multiplicative structuring, and pauses here to help students understand that doubling, and especially quadrupling, are multiplication processes.

The students in this group built each new batch on their previous work, but now that they are confident in their answers Catherine calls on a pair that will challenge the class to take a bigger leap: x16. Leaving the first chart on the board, Catherine knows that this visual will help scaffold for students who are struggling to follow the discussion and may even support students to discover a relationship between quadrupling a quadruple (1x4x4) and multiplying by 16.

Catherine encourages students to continue to explore connections on the ratio table. Perhaps the next student will suggest that they multiply the doubled batch by 8!

Minilesson: A String of Related Problems

This string is designed to help students continue to use multiplicative structuring, more flexibly converting one unit to another using strategies based on ratio thinking. Doing it after the congress instead of at the beginning of math workshop is beneficial today because the congress supported the ability to scale and this gives students a chance to practice what they were discussing.

Represent the problems on a t-chart like the one below, one problem at a time, moving from the top to the bottom of the chart, and invite students to share their conversion strategies. As they do, record their thinking on the t-chart.

The String:

Cups	Pints	Quarts	Gallons
			1
	4		
	2		
2			
160			
80			
	20		
	24		

Behind the Numbers

This string begins with 1 gallon, requiring students to scale using multiplication as they convert to smaller units. The next three rows are each half of the previous row; the computation is straightforward whether students scale based on the row above or convert units. 160 cups is 10 times the first row and 80 is half of 160, helping students realize that 80 cups is equal to 5 gallons. The next row emphasizes halving again but the final row challenges students to search for new connections. They may use the conversion relationships to find 24 pints equal 12 quarts and 3 gallons, or they may even combine 4 pints (½ gal.) with 20 pints (2 ½ gal.) The opportunities to move both laterally and vertically in these tables provide opportunities for rich discussions that will help students develop their proportional reasoning.

Reflections on the Day

Math workshop began today with a preparation for a gallery walk. As you moved around and conferred you may have noticed that more and more students are now starting to use ratio thinking. A congress provided students an opportunity to share strategies for scaling and explore the big idea that equivalent measurements can be exchanged. The minilesson was designed to encourage the use of ratio thinking, specifically the use of partial products and scaling. Each day you should see your children making progress on the landscape. Remember to document growth on the landscape in the overview. As this week continues, more ratio tables will be used for conversions, so keep the copies of Appendix D showing the equivalencies available.

DAY SEVEN

VANILLA COCOA-DUSTED TRUFFLES

Today begins with another minilesson designed to support multiplicative structuring and the flexible conversion of standard units of liquid volume. Then students work on another of Muffles' recipes: the vanilla cocoa-dusted truffles recipe. Once again students work on converting cups, pints, quarts, and gallons and ounces and pounds. This context also uses a ratio table as a tool, and as students work to generate recipes for larger batches, many opportunities will occur once again for rich discussions on equivalence and proportional reasoning related to measurement.

Day Seven Outline

Minilesson: A String of Related Problems

❖ Work on a string of related liquid volume problems designed to encourage students to convert fluently using multiplicative structuring.

Developing the Context

❖ Tell the story of Muffles' vanilla cocoa-dusted truffles, using Appendix F.

❖ Remind students of the equivalence of the units shown on Appendix D and ensure that they have a copy for reference.

❖ Ask students to work in pairs on Appendix F, making a recipe chart for various batches of Muffles' vanilla cocoa-dusted truffles.

Supporting the Investigation

❖ Confer with children as they work, noting the strategies they use and how they convert.

❖ As students finish, ask them to prepare a poster to convince others of their solutions and important things they have noticed along the way as they worked. These posters will be used on Day Eight in a gallery walk and congress.

Minilesson: A String of Related Problems

This string is designed in a similar fashion to the others you have been using throughout this unit. Its purpose as with the others is to keep familiarizing students with conversions. It also helps students use multiplicative structuring to convert more flexibly from one unit to another, using strategies based on proportional reasoning. Represent the problems on a t-chart like the one below, showing only one problem at a time, moving from the top to the bottom of the chart, and invite students to share their conversion strategies. As they do, record their thinking on the t-chart.

The String:

Cups	Pints	Quarts	Gallons
		2	
		4	
		8	
		12	
		32	
		16	
		10	
		15	

Behind the Numbers

This string begins with 2 quarts to foster a discussion of fractional representation—2 quarts out of 4 is 2/4 or ½ a gallon. 4 quarts provides an anchor reference for 1 gallon, and students are able to double for the next one and then triple or combine the double and single gallon for 12 quarts. 32 quarts requires scaling with multiplication up from 4 or 8 quarts or scaling using multiplication and division across the row. 16 encourages students to halve the results for 32. 10 and 15 quarts will require students to work flexibly with the equivalent units across the rows (or scale up from 2 quarts) and will reopen the discussion on fractions of a gallon; 10 quarts are 2 ½ gallons and 15 quarts are 3 ¾ gallons.

Inside One Classroom: A Portion of the Minilesson

Catherine (the teacher): 2 quarts. How many gallons would that be?

Josie: I know 4 quarts is a gallon. So we don't have enough for a gallon.

Catherine: True, but do we have a portion of a gallon? Since you used 4 quarts and I was going to do that one next anyway, I'll write down 4 quarts….and you said that was 1 gallon, right? So I'll write that down, too. So what should I put in the gallon column for 2 cups? Everyone, turn and talk to your shoulder partner.

Julia: It's half. 2 is half of 4.

Catherine: I've been listening in on some of your conversations and I think a lot of people

Author's notes

Catherine starts the minilesson by writing the first problem in the appropriate column. She asks about the gallons first to encourage the children to see that a portion of the gallon is filled, but only half of it. But because Josie has used the known equivalence of 4 quarts to 1 gallon, are agreeing with Julia. She said we should write ½ because 2 is half of 4. How many of you agree? *(Everyone's hands go up so Catherine writes ½ in the gallon column.)* Could I also write 2/4?

Sasha: Yes, It is 2 quarts out of 4 quarts. We could write that.

Catherine: So ½ is equal to 2/4? Can I use the equal sign?

Sasha: It must be. 2 quarts would fill the gallon halfway because 4 quarts fills it all of the way.

Josie: And there are 2 pints in a quart, so 4 pints make 2 quarts. I just doubled the 2. *(Catherine fills in the pints column with a 4.)*

Catherine: And so how many cups are in 4 pints?

Josh: *(looking at Appendix D)* 2 pints in a quart, so 2 quarts must be 4 pints and that is…..2, 4, 6, 8…., 8 cups.

Catherine: Ok, so if 8 cups is ½ gallon, could we use this information to figure out how many cups in the whole gallon…can we fill in the next row that Josie started?

Catherine goes on and adds this information to the chart as it now provides the children with other relationships they can consider, too. She provided pair talk next to give her students time to reflect on the relationships.

Writing 2/4 to represent 2 out of 4 cups introduces a common fraction with a part/parts model and it can now be compared to 1 out of 2 parts—the half.

The conversation continues focused on the equivalent relationships.

Developing the Context

Use Appendices D and F as you tell the following story. Remember to make the context come alive!

Muffles is very pleased with his new chart for his most popular recipe—dark chocolate truffles. He hung it up in the kitchen and now he and his assistant, Patricio, can make perfect bigger batches whenever they need to! He likes the idea so much that he decides he should make charts for some of his other truffle recipes. His vanilla cocoa-dusted truffles are also very popular so he decides to do this one next.

Because this type of truffle is not as popular, however, Muffles decides to do this chart differently. He does need as many truffles of this type so the sizes of his batches will be different. He starts a chart and writes the basic recipe down the first column. He starts working on his chart and fills in a few more things, but then the milk delivery truck pulls up. "Not now," thinks Muffles. "I haven't finished with my chart!"

Patricio offers to finish it for Muffles and so Muffles leaves to deal with the milk delivery. Patricio thinks finishing the chart will be easy. He'll do it the same way Muffles did the chart for his dark chocolate truffles. But then Patricio notices that the chart is different. There are no headings on this chart, except The Basic Recipe and The Big Batch. And there is no Very Big Batch even on the chart! "Uh-oh...," thinks Patricio. "I'm in trouble... I've got another problem to crack. How do I know if Muffles was going to triple, or quadruple? Maybe he wasn't..."

Remind children that the basic recipe is in ounces and cups but with bigger batches they might want to use different units of measure to save time. Make sure they understand that this chart may have some aspects similar to the other, but it may also be different. Suggest they look very carefully at the clues Muffles left for Patricio and remind them of the equivalent units listed on Appendix D: 1 pound = 16 ounces; 2 cups = 1 pint; 2 pints = 1 quart; and 4 quarts = 1 gallon.

Assign math partners and send students off to investigate what Patricio should write on this new chart.

Behind the Numbers

This investigation is much more difficult than the one introduced on Day Five as the headings are missing. It is not possible to tell how much to scale the basic recipe up by using the heading as the scale factor. In two columns the number of truffles is not even given. The only way students can determine the scaling factor is to determine the ratio of the ingredients given. If 4 ounces of white chocolate are need for the basic recipe, then 1 lb. (in the third column) means Muffles was quadrupling the recipe in this column. By now students should be more comfortable with the ratio table as a tool. Encourage them to jump around and do what they know first. For example, if they do the Big Batch first, that might help with the column where Muffles has written 150 truffles, as that is half of the Big Batch. Samples of children's work from field testing are provided in *Supporting the Investigation* to help you anticipate what your children might do.

Supporting the Investigation

As you move around conferring, take note of how children are moving on the table. Look for children who just assume this chart will be the same ratios as the chart they made on Day Five and Six. Do they just write Doubling, Tripling, and Quadrupling across the top without looking at the numbers given in the columns? For example, see the work sample in Figure 5. At first the student writes in the headings doubling, tripling, and quadrupling. However, as she works to complete the chart she makes use of the ratio of the ingredients.

As you confer with students who do this, query them afterward about whether their original headings worked. In this case the child has written x2, x4, x5, and x6. These are new headings that reflect Muffles' notes and the student's discoveries as she worked. Challenge students like this to explain how their thinking changed, and why.

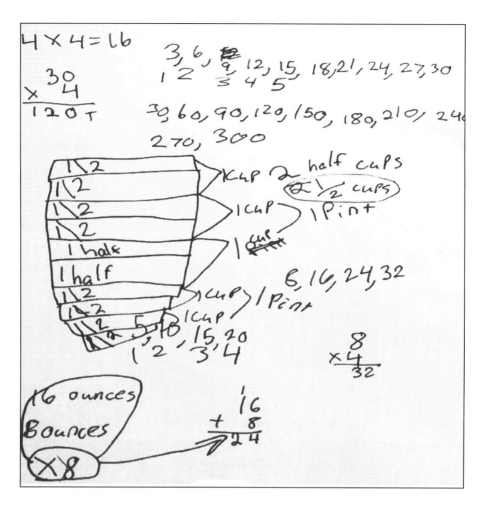

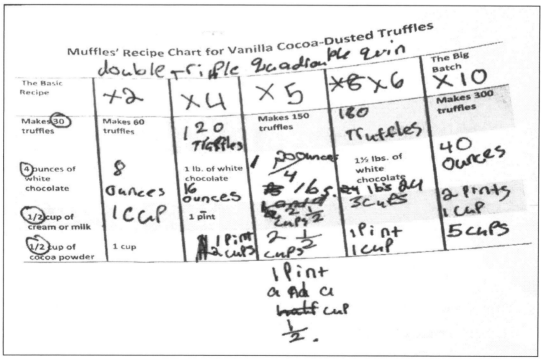

Figure 5: Work on the vanilla cocoa-dusted truffles

Reflections on the Day

Today you likely saw a lot of progress during this difficult investigation. Without the headings, children really had to examine the proportionality of the ingredients. Although they may have had to think hard about this, the difficulty level most likely challenged them in a beneficial way to examine relationships. Tomorrow the relationships noticed will become the focus of discussion in a gallery walk and the congress.

DAY EIGHT

THE CHART FOR THE TRUFFLES

Materials Needed

Students' work from Day Seven

Sticky notes
(approximately 3 per student)

Today begins with a minilesson on converting ounces to pounds. Students then add finishing touches to their posters from Day Seven and a gallery walk ensues. After the gallery walk a congress is held to more deeply discuss a few of the pieces, such as scaling and using a ratio table as a tool.

Day Eight Outline

Minilesson: A String of Related Problems

❖ Work on a string of related problems designed to encourage students to convert ounces to pounds fluently using the ratio table as a tool for thinking.

❖ Introduce number pairs as another way to represent the data.

Facilitating the Gallery Walk

❖ Confer with children as they put finishing touches to their posters, asking them to consider the most important things they want to tell their audience about smart ways to convert.

❖ Conduct a Gallery Walk to allow students time to reflect and comment on each other's posters on the investigation started on Day Seven.

Facilitating the Math Congress

❖ Convene students at the meeting area to discuss a few important ideas about converting efficiently from one unit of measure to another.

Minilesson: A String of Related Problems

This string is designed in a similar fashion to the others you have been using throughout this unit. Its purpose as with the others is to keep familiarizing students with conversions. Today the focus is ounces to pounds. Represent the problems on a t-chart like the one below, showing only one problem at a time, moving from the top to the bottom of the chart, and invite students to share their conversion strategies. As they do, record their thinking on the t-chart.

The String:

Ounces	Pounds (lbs.)
16	
8	
4	
12	
32	
24	
48	
160	

Since this ratio table has only 2 columns, as children produce the pounds for each of the problems, this is a nice time to introduce number pairs as another way of modeling the data: (16, 1), (8, ½), (4, ¼), etc. You can just explain that mathematicians sometimes represent the numbers on a ratio table that way. They think about the numbers as input/output and they pair the input with the output.

Facilitating the Gallery Walk

Ask students to return to the posters they began on Day Seven, adding any finishing touches they desire. As they work, move around and confer, asking them to consider the most important things they want to tell their audience about smart ways to convert. Remind them that it is not necessary to write about everything they did, but instead to concentrate on convincing their audience about the important things they discovered and want to defend.

Two posters are shown here large scale so that you can see the kinds of notes students at this age make during gallery walks. Notes from Figure 6.1 are transcribed below, with spelling corrected for readability:

"I love how you labeled a lot."

"I don't get how you got 1 cup in the very big batch was ½ cup. Because it would be x2…"

"Yours is good!!!!"

"You did something similar to what I did."

"I notice that you did a lot of table diagrams"

"I like how you did the chart. Also you did the same as me."

"I notice you took your time and showed all of your thinking! I love how it is so neat! Love the Poster!"

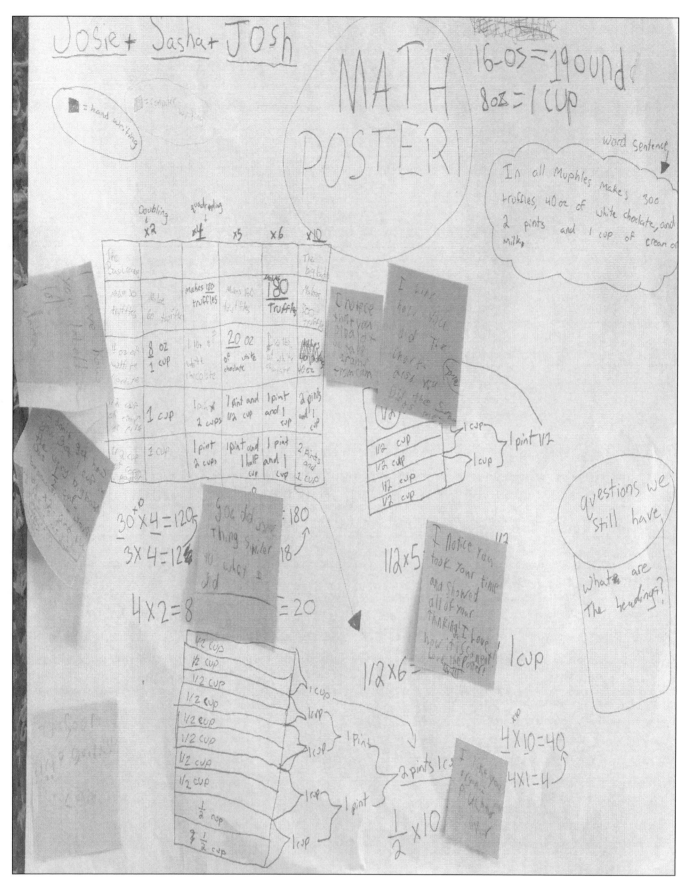

Figure 6.1: From the gallery walk

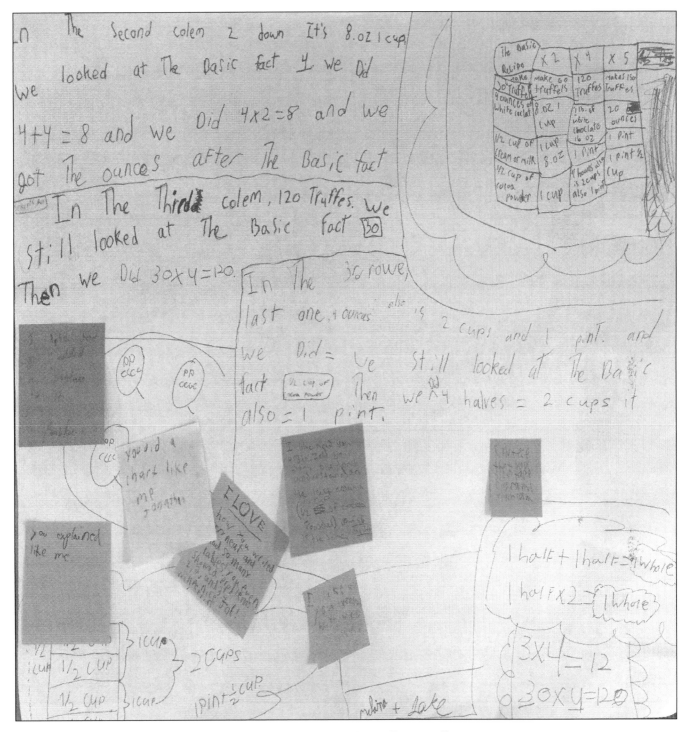

Figure 6.2: From the gallery walk

"I like how you added a sentence for it."

"You explained like me."

"You did a chart like me."

"I LOVE how you writed very neat and had so many labels! You even showed problems 1, 2 and 3. Nice job!"

"I like how you organized your work but don't understand on the last column (1/2 cup of cocoa powder) your x5 is the same."

"I like [how] you explained with words."

"I notice that you did a table diagram!"

One of the interesting things to note about the comments is how students are beginning to read each other's arguments. Several of the notes left on the posters refer to how similar models are being used (by the reviewer and the author of the poster). One note in particular is important to point out. Griffin has left a note on the poster shown in Figure 6.2 saying, "I don't understand. On the last column ("½ cup of cocoa powder) x5 is the same." He has noted how the Basic Recipe calls for ½ cup of milk and ½ cup of cocoa powder and thus the last column on the poster should be 2.5 cups for both the milk and the cocoa powder. He has read the poster so carefully. This is evidence of the ability to read a mathematical argument—one of the CCSS Standards of Mathematical Practice.

Facilitating the Math Congress

Review the posters and choose a few that you can use for a discussion that will deepen understanding and support growth along the landscape of learning described in the overview. There is not necessarily one best plan for a congress. There are many different plans that might all be supportive of development.

You'll want to make this congress supportive of the use of the ratio table as a tool: jumping around on it in clever ways for converting and using equivalent rates. Look for student work that exhibits big ideas about multiplication, equivalent rates, and proportional reasoning, and notice whose work might be used to target strategies, such as scaling and using partial products with the ratio table as a tool for thinking. Remember to work developmentally and think about how to scaffold your congress. Think about how you might use the congress so that the discussion that occurs actually promotes new insights.

Reflections on the Day

Math workshop began today with a minilesson on converting ounces to pounds. Students were introduced to number pairs as another way to model the data on the charts. In the gallery walk and subsequent congress you may have noticed that more and more students are now using proportional reasoning. Are they able to use generalized scaling, or just doubling? Each day you should see your children making progress on the landscape. Remember to document the growth on the landscape—the learning pathway of each child.

DAY NINE

PRICES BY THE POUND

Materials Needed

The Price Chart
(Appendix G, one per
pair of students)

Pencils

**Drawing paper or
several sheets of copy
paper**

**Blank Chart Paper for
posters** (sticky note
style is best as it
makes taping on the
walls unnecessary)

Markers

$\mathbb{T}$oday begins with another minilesson on converting ounces to pounds. Following the minilesson a new context is developed. Muffles has decided to sell his truffles in little bags by the pound, not just in boxes. He weighs his dark chocolate truffles and he finds that 64 of his truffles weigh 1 pound. What does each truffle weigh and how much should he charge?

Day Nine Outline

Minilesson: A String of Related Problems

❖ Work on a string of related problems designed to encourage students to convert ounces to pounds fluently using the ratio table as a tool for thinking.

Developing the Context

❖ Use Appendix G and tell the story of Muffles' Price Chart.
❖ Send students off in pairs to work on the chart.

Supporting the Investigation

❖ Move around the room supporting and challenging where needed.
❖ Celebrate the strategies you see and then convene students at the meeting area to discuss a few important ideas about converting efficiently from one unit of measure to another.
❖ Ensure that a final group consensus exists for the numbers on the chart as it will be needed on Day Ten.

Minilesson: A String of Related Problems

This string is designed in a similar fashion to the others you have been using throughout this unit. Its purpose, as with the others, is to keep familiarizing students with conversions. It also helps students use multiplicative structuring to convert more flexibly from one unit to another, using strategies based on proportional reasoning. Represent the problems on a ratio table like the one below, showing only one problem at a time, moving from the top to the bottom of the model, and invite students to share their conversion strategies. As they do, record their thinking on the t-chart.

The String:

Cupcakes	Pounds (lbs.)	Ounces
12	1	
24		
6		
3		
30		
9		

Developing the Context

Use Appendix G as you tell the following story. If you have a smart board, you can display the image. Remember to make the context come alive!

> Muffles is very pleased with his new charts. Now he and his assistant, Patricio, can make perfect bigger batches whenever they need to and the line of customers can move quickly along, without long waits. Most importantly, the last person in the line won't have to worry that when he or she gets to the counter the dark chocolate and the vanilla cocoa-dusted truffles will be gone.
>
> Muffles also has another idea—one that he has been thinking about for a while. He has always sold his delicious truffles in boxes of 10 for $10 dollars. But, maybe customers would prefer to buy little bags of truffles with cute ribbons and he could charge by weight. This would save him time and money. Patricio wouldn't have to put truffles in so many boxes—that would certainly save time. And he wouldn't have to buy so many boxes either—and that would also save money!
>
> Muffles starts to make a new chart—a price chart! He makes three columns: one for the weight in ounces, one for the weight in pounds, and one for the cost.
>
> Muffles begins filling in his new chart. He writes in the first row: 64 truffles, 16 ounces, 1 pound. Then in the ounces column, under the 16, he writes, 8, 4, 2, 1, ½. "I will charge

$2.50 an ounce for my truffles," Muffles thinks to himself, and so he writes that on the new price chart, too, in the row where it says 1 ounce.

But just as Muffles was about to continue, the delivery truck bringing chocolate came. "Patricio will need to finish this," he thought to himself. "Patricio….where are you? I need some help! I have another job for you…"

Assign math partners and send students off to investigate what Patricio should write on this new chart.

Supporting the Investigation

As you move around conferring, take note of how children are moving on the ratio table. The halving of the ounces should help them. Today is a good day to celebrate as you move around: celebrate how easily children are moving around the chart. It is likely that a gallery walk and congress will not be necessary today (unless you see that some children are still challenged in which case do take the time, as the discussion will continue to help them). If children are using flexible strategies and everyone seems comfortable using the ratio relationships, just have a brief discussion and ensure there is group consensus on the prices on the chart as tomorrow children will make their own charts and they will need the data on this one.

Reflections on the Day

Math workshop began today with a minilesson on converting ounces to pounds. Children then continued to work with these conversions as they developed a price chart for Muffles. Throughout this unit children have been supported to develop the use of the ratio table as a powerful model and tool for conversions of units of measure, but also for multiplication. Today is a day to celebrate with them on the variety of strategies they have developed. Tomorrow their learning can be extended as they develop their own pricing charts and choose their own numbers.

DAY TEN

CHOOSE YOUR OWN NUMBERS

Materials Needed

Pencils

Drawing paper or several sheets of copy paper

Blank Chart Paper for posters (sticky note style is best as it makes taping on the walls unnecessary)

Markers

Today begins with another minilesson on converting ounces to pounds. Following the minilesson children are invited to add numbers of their own choosing to the price chart. Today is a chance to get further evidence on each child's facility with measurement conversions and their ability to use the ratio table as a tool for thinking. Let them inquire and challenge themselves. Big numbers, fractions, anything goes! But encourage them to pick numbers where they can use relationships!

Day Ten Outline

Minilesson: A String of Related Problems

❖ Work on a string of related problems designed to encourage students to convert ounces to pounds fluently using the ratio table as a tool for thinking.

Developing the Context

❖ Explain how proud you are of the many strategies everyone has developed over the last two weeks. Point out how powerful the ratio table is as a model for measurement conversions.

❖ Suggest they use all of the strategies they have developed to add more numbers to the price chart.

Supporting the Investigation

❖ Move around and confer, remembering to clarify what you see, celebrate the strategies you see children trying, and support and challenge as needed.

Minilesson: A String of Related Problems

This string is designed in a similar fashion to the others you have been using throughout this unit. Its purpose, as with the others, is to keep familiarizing students with conversions. Represent the problems on a ratio table like the one below, showing only one problem at a time, moving from the top to the bottom of the chart, and invite students to share their conversion strategies. These numbers will remind them of the chart they did on Day Nine so make sure those papers are not available. Using the same numbers is purposeful to ensure everyone is comfortable when they go off to work on the subsequent investigation. Leave the results of the minilesson, the finished chart, up on the board so that children can make use of it as they work.

Ounces	Pounds	Cost
16	1	$40
8		
4		
2		
1		
1/2		

Developing the Context

Explain that since this is the last day of the unit, you think it might be fun for everyone to add other numbers of their choosing to Muffles' price chart. Provide them with drawing paper so that they can make their own ratio table, but provide as a constraint that they have to use Muffles' rate: 1 ounce costs $2.50. Tell them they can pick the numbers and should challenge themselves, but remind them to make use of relationships and to use the variety of strategies they have developed. Point out that the chart from the minilesson is still up and they have their work from Day Nine, then assign math partners and send students off to choose their own numbers.

Supporting the Investigation

As you move around conferring, take note of how children are moving on the ratio table. Note how they challenge themselves. Do they use partial products to find numbers other than the ones on the chart? Do they use generalized scaling? If you like you can challenge students to add more columns and convert the cost in dollars to all quarters, or all dimes.

Reflections on the Unit

The mathematician Samuel Karlin once said, "The purpose of models is not to fit the data but to sharpen the questions." In this unit, the ratio table and the double number line were developed and used to sharpen students' questions. Students constructed proportional reasoning; they used partial products and scaling. With these models, equivalence and measurement conversions took on new meanings.

The models were developed through a number of different investigations. Students explored the length of the line of customers and placed signs along the way in ten minute intervals to show the rate of time to length and the number of customers. They formulated various strategies for making equivalent measurements using the Customary U.S. measurements for length, then later for liquid volume and weight as they scaled up Muffles' recipes to make larger batches. They even examined ratios with fractional amounts.

Often mathematics has been taught in our schools as if it were a dead language. It was something that mathematicians had created in the past—something that needed to be learned, practiced, and applied. When the definition of mathematics shifts toward the activity of mathematizing one's own lived world, the constructive nature of the discipline and its connection to problem solving become clear.

"Which tool should I use?" asks Patricio.

Patricio decides to use a tape measure. He pulls it all of the way out until he gets to the end and very carefully marks the sidewalk with a pencil at the end, and then lines the tape measure up at the mark and starts again. He has to do this 6 times because the line is so long!

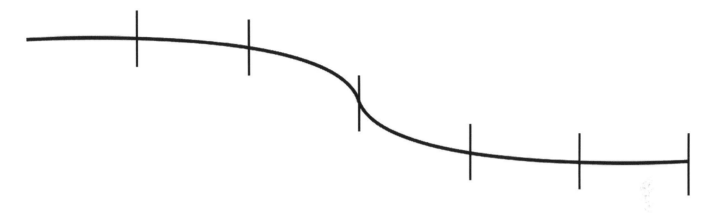

Patricio runs in and tells Muffles with excitement, "The line is 6 tape measures long!"

Muffles looks puzzled. "But how long *is* that?" he asks. "How many feet is the line? How many yards? How many inches? Or, is the tape measure in centimeters?" Tape measures come in all different sizes. I can't tell the reporter that the line is 6 tape measures long!

Patricio looks again at the tape measure. He pulls it all of the way out and notices that it ends at 60 inches. "Hmmm...so each of my marks is 60 inches," Patricio thinks to himself. "But how long is the line?"

Patricio's tape measure is 60 inches long. He used it 6 times.

Conversion Tables

Inches	Feet
12	1

Feet	Yards
3	1

How many feet is the line?

How many yards?

How many inches?

The next morning people read the reporter's story about Muffles and his truffles and when Patricio got to work the line was really, really long! Customers at the end of the line began to complain and wanted to know approximately how long they would have to wait to get to the counter. Now Patricio had another measurement mystery to solve!

That night when he and Muffles closed up the shop, Patricio had an idea. He thought, "Whenever I feel stuck with a math problem, I know that if I try to model it somehow I have a way to start." So when he got home he built a model. In the morning he brought his model and a small clock to the shop. He also borrowed a very big tape measure from a friend who was a carpenter. It was 120 inches long! He brought that too because he thought if he measured with something that was very long he wouldn't have as much work to do. The shop opened at 10 AM.

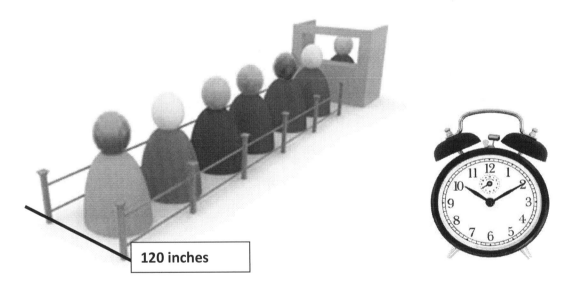

120 inches

When he got to the shop, Patricio measured quickly and made his lines again. He had six lines again, just like before, but this time each section was 120 inches because he had used a very long tape measure. Patricio watched the clock as the customers gradually got to the counter. The man with the cool Panama hat had been standing with his heels just touching the first mark that Patricio had made with his tape measure and soon the man was at the counter. Patricio thought, "Ah ha! It had taken 10 minutes for the man to move 120 inches. So, about 6 people every 120 inches, and that takes about 10 minutes," Patricio thought. He put a sign up on that mark that said, "10 minutes to the counter."

Next Patricio drew a long line to represent the line of customers and he began marking where the signs for every 10 minutes should go.

10 minutes

120 inches

Help Patricio finish modeling the problem. How long is this new line of customers and how long will it take for the last customer in line to get to the counter? (Remember, there are 60 minutes in an hour and 60 seconds in a minute.)

Inches	Feet	Minutes	Seconds	Hours	People
120		10			6

Is Patricio's model a helpful tool for solving the problem?

How did you use it?

Appendix D: Conversion Chart

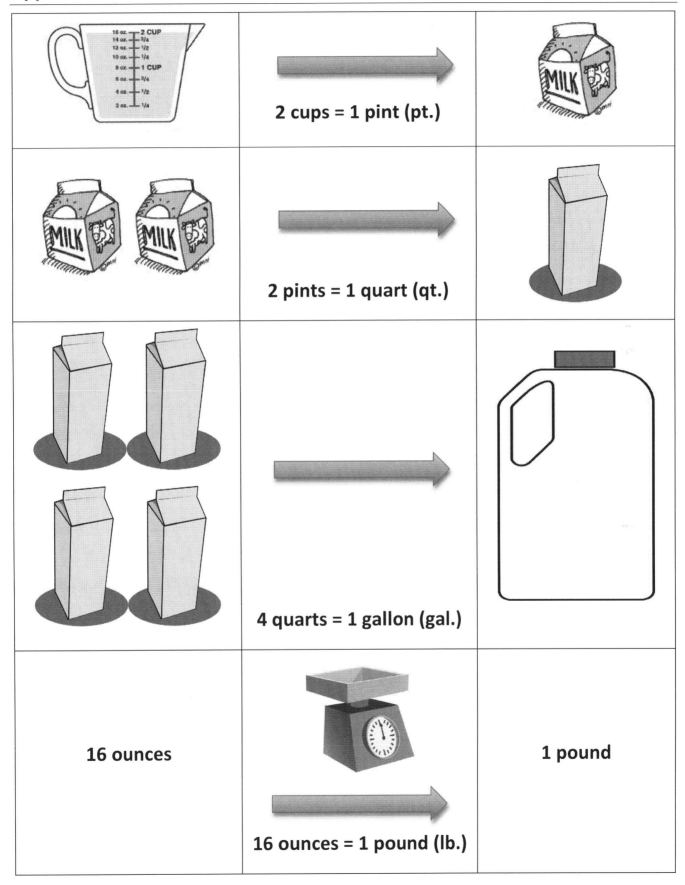

2 cups = 1 pint (pt.)

2 pints = 1 quart (qt.)

4 quarts = 1 gallon (gal.)

16 ounces

16 ounces = 1 pound (lb.)

1 pound

Appendix E: Muffles' Recipe Chart for Dark Chocolate Truffles

The Basic Recipe	Doubling	Tripling	Quadrupling	The Big Batch	The VERY Big Batch
Makes 60 truffles	Makes 120 truffles			Makes 600 truffles	
10 ounces of dark chocolate					
1 cup of cream or milk					1 gallon of cream or milk

Appendix F: Muffles' Recipe Chart for Vanilla Cocoa-Dusted Truffles

The Basic Recipe					The Big Batch
Makes 30 truffles	Makes 60 truffles		Makes 150 truffles		Makes 300 truffles
4 ounces of white chocolate		1 lb. of white chocolate		1 ½ lbs. of white chocolate	
½ cup of cream or milk					
½ cup cocoa powder	1 cup	1 pint			

The Price Chart

Truffles	Ounces	Pound	Price
64	16	1	
	8		
	4		
	1		$2.50
	½		

Made in the USA
Columbia, SC
07 January 2019